THE LAT
FOR YOU

THE LATEST HELP
FOR YOUR NERVES

Dr Claire Weekes

Thorsons
An Imprint of HarperCollins*Publishers*

Thorsons
An Imprint of HarperCollins*Publishers*
77–85 Fulham Palace Road,
Hammersmith, London W6 8JB
1160 Battery Street,
San Francisco, California 94111–1213

First published in Australia by
Angus & Robertson Publishers 1989
First published in the United Kingdom by
Angus & Robertson (UK) 1989
Published by Thorsons 1995
1 3 5 7 9 10 8 6 4 2

A catalogue record for this book
is available from the British Library

ISBN 0 7225 3200 8

Printed in Great Britain by
HarperCollinsManufacturing Glasgow

Contents

To Marcel and Cecily Aurousseau
There is a lifetime of meaning in those two names.

1

First, I Want to Say

Over the last 26 years, since retiring from active medical practice (in 1963), I have written four books on nervous illness, which are well known worldwide.

Before I retired I was a physician. That's the kind of doctor who treats physical illness as distinct from surgical and nervous illness. However, physicians are sometimes asked to treat nervously ill patients and it is essential for them to know how to do this, or at least to know where to refer the patients satisfactorily.

Gradually over the years, nervously ill people came to me for help, many of whom were acutely ill although they had been treated previously, some for a long time, by orthodox psychiatrists. Indeed, I saw so many of these suffering people that I began to question the use of the psychiatric treatment commonly given in those days: Freudian psychoanalysis.

Treatment by psychoanalysis often called for a search for possible subconscious causes, a search which could demand weeks, months, even years. Not only were anxious, apprehensive people sometimes warned of the necessity of such long searching, the encouraging word "cure" was rarely used. It was even purposely avoided.

The symptoms of nervous illness (used here to mean the anxiety state) felt by these people were often so upsetting that many sufferers came asking for urgent relief. These symptoms included: attacks of panic, rapidly beating heart, weakness, fatigue, trembling, a feeling of difficulty in swallowing solid food, of taking a deep breath, and so on. Can you imagine such people's bewilderment and despair on being told of the possibility of lengthy investigation for a hidden cause?

Indeed, I became so concerned that I found a way of not only giving a quick relief of symptoms but also of giving a practical program for recovery. I even mentioned "cure". (I am talking about the anxiety state, mentioned earlier.)

In an anxiety state, the sufferer is more or less constantly anxious, afraid—especially afraid of the symptoms his "aroused", "sensitised" nerves have brought. The original arousal has often been caused by some stressful life situation. However, I often found that in time many nervously ill people were no longer concerned with the original cause of their stress. They were more concerned with the state they were now in (the "way they felt") and with "what could happen next"! This was why they felt they needed urgent help.

Some had even become agoraphobic. That is, they suffered incapacitating fear away from the safety of home, particularly in crowded places—anywhere where they believed they could not make a quick escape or get help quickly should their fears, as they thought, grow beyond them. This fear included travelling, especially in a vehicle they could not stop at will.

I was not then, and am not now, afraid to use the word "cure", because I explain my meaning of "cure". I do not mean that the sufferer would not feel nervous symptoms again. I explain that the symptoms of nervous illness are no more than the symptoms of stress and that while we live we must feel stress symptoms from time to time. However, because I show how to cope with these symptoms and give a practical program for recovery, people learn to be no longer frightened or bewildered by them.

The basis of my teaching has always been to show how to heal oneself, so that one develops an inner voice of confidence that is born from the experience of having been through the fire and having brought oneself out of it!

This book differs from those four books* mentioned earlier, because it is confined to the interviews and talks I have given in public during the last six years.

A patient once said, "Why don't you write it all down, Doctor? That would save you going over it with each of us?" So I did.

My first book, *Self Help for Your Nerves* (called *Hope and Help for Your Nerves* in the United States), was published in 1962 and was a success overnight. After that, whenever I spoke on radio or television, whatever the country, the relief of listeners was almost palpable. Today, 1989, the work is accepted, used and recommended by doctors and other therapists, and by thousands of nervous people worldwide. The need for quick relief is now well recognised.

---

* *Self Help for Your Nerves*; *Peace from Nervous Suffering*; *Simple, Effective Treatment of Agoraphobia*; and *More Help for Your Nerves*.

Six Interviews on BBC Television, England, 1983

In 1983, I was asked to give a series of talks on the BBC television program "Pebble Mill at One", which was broadcast throughout the British Isles from Birmingham each day, at lunchtime. I agreed to give six talks, one to be broadcast weekly.

At that time I was 80, and this offer gave me a welcome chance to present a bird's-eye view of my work on nervous illness over the last 40 years, including especially the work done during the last 25 years, when I had concentrated on helping nervous people.

To be able to present a comprehensive, yet concise, review of the whole range of my work to people throughout the British Isles was a chance I could not resist, in spite of wondering how my memory would cope in its eightieth year! Fran Groves, one of the BBC producers of the talks, and who had persuaded me to give them, had no doubt about the memory. I did. At 80 one is very open to doubt! I wasn't afraid of forgetting what had happened over the last 40 years—I knew that so well. I was afraid of forgetting what I had just said half a minute ago! The prospect of stumbling and admitting that I couldn't remember my last sentence was bad enough before friends, but to forget before millions of people throughout the British Isles was quite something else!

However, there were precautions I could take, and I took them. For six weeks before the first broadcast I walked the streets of London, head down, gesticulating, reciting each talk over and over, making sure there would be no memory slips.

I summarised each talk on large cards, and found that I would have to remember only the look of a card and the words would come. This preparation did not fail.

The six talks have now been made into a video for which the BBC has given me world rights.

My interviewer was Marian Foster, who is a Geordie. That means that she comes from Tyneside in the north-east of England; it also means that her interviews were penetrating and yet as sympathetic as one could hope for. Thank you, Marian.

For Anne, my ex-patient, to appear on television with me before millions of compatriots took astounding courage. She had so much desire to save others from the suffering she had known that she readily put their suffering before her own comfort. Her story was given so simply, honestly and intelligently, that she may have helped thousands with it. Thank you, Anne.

I suppose I should have offered these six talks here casually and unemotionally, but I did not give them casually. Giving them was a special event in my life.

TALK NO. 1.
THE PATTERN

Introduction by Marian Foster

Every day thousands of men and women all over the world have their lives ruined by nervous illness. It can manifest itself by a "not quite coping with life" feeling or, at its most extreme, it can cripple the sufferer, often ruining his life and that of his family, as loved ones try to cope with a mass of confusing symptoms which can accompany the anxiety state.

Many nervously ill people and their families have suffered in this way for years, until they have found help in the teachings of a doctor who has become internationally acclaimed for her understanding and treatment of nervous illness: Dr Claire Weekes. Through her books and tapes she has helped literally thousands of patients worldwide with her deep insight into the cause of nervous illness and her compassionate understanding of the simple route to recovery. She teaches people that they have often become trapped in nervous suffering by worrying more about the "state they are in"—the symptoms themselves—than the original cause of their illness.

Over the last few years, I have interviewed Dr Weekes on a number of occasions about her life's work in treating nervous illness; this compilation of those talks represents a unique record of Dr Weekes's approach to treating the anxiety state, including depression, obsessions and phobias.

But first we meet Anne, our patient: her pattern of illness began simply but progressed unchecked into the misery of an obsessional anxiety.

PATIENT: You can't get rid of an obsession by staying in

the house, or going out, as you can with some phobias. If you've got agoraphobia, you can get a measure of relief when you're not fighting it all the time, but with obsessions you can't, because they're in your head and you carry them around wherever you go—sleeping and waking they're there! And they're not as big as life, they're ten times larger, more frightening. They go on and on until you think they can't go on any longer and they still do!

MARIAN: Anne is just one of the many thousands helped from nervous breakdown to full recovery by the teachings of Dr Claire Weekes. I asked Dr Weekes how her interest developed in the early years.

DOCTOR: First of all, I was a physician—that's an ordinary doctor—and I learnt fairly soon that to help people—and I like people, that's another thing—you have to give them as much peace of mind as you can as quickly as you can. If you can send the patient away with peace of mind, half the battle is won; so that gradually got me the reputation of being the sort of doctor who was interested in the nervous reaction of her patients.

MARIAN: Have all your books and teaching come through your own experiences as a doctor, or have you done any specialist training, the way psychiatrists would have done?

DOCTOR: I had the usual psychiatric training that we all get as we go through Medicine, but then I had myself been nervously exhausted and I learned a lot from that, especially when I got myself out of it. So I found out what it was like to be nervously exhausted and how to recover from it unaided. You see, I started Medicine when I was 37—before that I studied Science and so I was able to bring to Medicine, I think, perhaps a more mature attitude than if I had started at 19, as the majority do. I'd come to know people and I liked people, and I think that all combined to help me as a doctor. I was not just the sort of general practitioner looking after people's coughs and colds, but a doctor who tried to look after the whole person, including any particular nervous suffering.

MARIAN: So what was the difference between the advice that you were giving to people and advice that perhaps psychiatrists were giving? Did you have a very different technique? Is your method very different?

DOCTOR: Yes, it is different . . . in fact, when my first book came out it was described by one of the psychiatrists in Sydney [where I was practising] as "home-spun philosophy" and I suppose it's just commonsense. I had to see it work: as a GP I not only saw the patients when they came to me with some nervous problem, but I also saw them when they came over the years with their ordinary coughs and colds and headaches, so I was able to see if my work had succeeded or not. I think the years I spent doing research work as a scientist helped me very much to analyse what was happening to a patient and to see the simplicity that lay behind the whole pattern of their nervous suffering. I think that being a scientist first helped, because I looked for the trunk of the tree, I wasn't led away by the leaves and the branches; I was able to pick, I thought, the most important part of an illness and people's reactions.

MARIAN: Now over the next few weeks you're going to be giving us a lot of your sound, "home-spun" commonsense advice about how to look after our own nervousness, how to cope with it. And we're going to see too, one lady, one patient, whom you have helped—but did you work with her alone, or were you working with her doctor?

DOCTOR: Because I'm retired now and not in practice,

nervously ill people communicate with me mainly by telephone, or letter—and not too much of either now, I hope—but if they do I often get in touch with their doctor, because I find that when I do this I sometimes get a lot of good cooperation, and especially with the doctor of this patient whom we'll be showing. Before we put her on the film, I rang her doctor and said, "Have I your OK to do this?" And he said, "You know, a few years ago I would have hesitated, but not now . . . I think that she is so outstanding that she should be shown to other people, to help them."

MARIAN: Let's see now an excerpt from the conversation that this woman had with us and we can see just how bad the situation was for her, some time ago.

PATIENT: . . . I'd had desensitisation and relaxation; that helped. I even tried hypnosis, but that didn't work, because I don't hypnotise (some people do, some don't) . . . I mean, everything going, I've had. But it didn't work. So once they started talking about leucotomy [an operation on the brain] I thought, "That's it, I'll never have that!" because as a teenager I knew someone who had had a leucotomy and I'd thought from then onwards that I'd die first, as it hadn't been successful, and when they started talking about it to me, I thought, "That's it, I've had enough. I'm going!"

MARIAN: There we are: an example of despair that this patient went through. But how were you able to help her?

DOCTOR: Marian, the others who had tried—and had tried so hard—had picked on complications: they'd told her she was an aggressive type; they'd gone for difficult explanations. I went for the simple one: I explained to her that the obsessions that were upsetting her so much were no more than upsetting thoughts repeated in a tired mind. Now, she could grasp that. And that was the truth, that's all it was. She grasped it and I taught her how to bypass the obsessive thoughts and to glimpse the truth, if only for a few moments each day; she was seeing the truth for a few moments daily. And that's what she practised. That's what cured her.

MARIAN: And how long did it take her before she was back on her feet again?

DOCTOR: Well, it's hard to remember because I was only in contact with her on the phone. You know, I only saw Anne once; it was all done through a tape recording and the telephone. I would say it took Anne about 12 months before she felt happy and at ease with her obsessions; happy to be alive again. I'd say about 12 months.

MARIAN: Is this what makes your work unique? The fact that you go through, that you cut away all the bits that are confusing and you go through to find the simple remedy?

DOCTOR: I think that's it, Marian, I do. I try to give the patient an understanding of the simplicity and then a program with which he can follow the simple route back to normal thinking, normal intensity of feeling.

MARIAN: Is that what you're going to do for us, over the next few weeks?

DOCTOR: Yes, I'm going to do it not only for the people who are nervously ill, not only open their eyes to the simplicity and the simple plan for recovery, but for other people who have never been nervously ill, so that they will lose the feeling of mystery in nervous illness, and they will be no longer afraid to talk about it, read about it or even to listen to me talk now—there must be no mystery about nervous illness, because there is none really. I mean the anxiety state, of course. It is a simple pattern of development, an almost inevitable pattern of development, and of course recovery just lies in reversing the pattern.

TALK No. 2.

THE ANXIETY STATE

MARIAN: The subject today is the anxiety state, Doctor, and is that the crux of the whole problem of nervous illness?

DOCTOR: It's the commonest kind of nervous illness, Marian. It really means a person who is, one could say, possessed with anxiety, which turns to fear. In my experience there are two main kinds: there is the person whose anxiety has come about because of some specific problem, perhaps including sorrow, guilt or disgrace. The sufferer knows what caused the anxiety originally and tries to grapple with the cause.

Then there's the person who has been put under temporary stress, perhaps by some sudden physical strain—say, a severe haemorrhage, an accident or perhaps a stress that in itself is no longer important. As a doctor I found the majority of my nervously ill patients were like this, with no specific problem; they had become much more afraid of the *state they were in* than of any original problem.

To understand that, we have to understand that our nervous system has two main parts: one we call "voluntary" and we use it to move our muscles as we will; and the other we call "involuntary"—it controls the functioning of our organs and the registering of our emotions. When under stress, emotions are registered, maybe at first simply, with the strength one would normally experience, but gradually, if stress progresses, the registering of emotions becomes exaggerated and we say that our nerves are "aroused". This may be a very painful experience. It means that an ordinary spasm of fear can become a flash of panic; just feeling a heartbeart can become a consciousness of the "bang–bang–bang" of each beat; or, as a patient may say, he feels "missed" heartbeats, churning stomach, inability to swallow, an inability to take in a deep breath, a feeling of weakness, or almost of fainting. These are difficult, upsetting symptoms to live with, and they're the symptoms of stress.

Now, the sufferer invariably makes the mistake of adding more stress by becoming afraid of those symptoms; what's more, he doesn't understand them and this adds further to stress. He's in a cycle: stress originally through the haemorrhage or the accident or whatever it was, then the added stress of his fear, and so, more stress symptoms. And there you have the cycle turning and through that comes what I call, not so much "arousal" (that's the scientific term) but sensitisation. The first thing to do to help the patient is to reverse that cycle. It was simple; its development was simple; the cure is simple, too. *I did not say "easy"*, I said *"simple"*. First, to reverse the cycle, give him understanding of the symptoms.

MARIAN: How effective is that understanding? Do you find that people respond to that quickly?

DOCTOR: Some do, some don't. One woman who had been afraid to leave her home, who would not even go shopping unless accompanied, had only one consultation and was completely cured. She came back to me and said, "It's gone—I can't panic, no matter what I do. I went to the top of the [14-storey] AMP building, but I can't panic any more!" One visit with a new understanding cured her. But for most people, the understanding has to be helped with a program for recovery.

Can I explain to you just how complicated some of these symptoms of stress can seem? Take the trembling hands: when a person under great stress finds that his hands are beginning to tremble, he thinks that is the sign of a great deterioration, that he must be becoming organically involved now . . . "You're losing your control! You're losing control, old man!", but actually it can be explained as simply as the knee-jerk reaction. If you tap a person's knee and the leg extends, that is because in the tendon of the tapped muscle there are nerve endings that send messages to the spine and back saying "Jerk", like that [*Doctor taps her knee*]. In the muscles of the fingers there are nerve endings which do the same to the finger muscles. Those nerve endings are acted on by adrenalin, which is one of the stress hormones liberated by that part of the nervous system that controls the organs and the emotions. Adrenalin stimulates nerves that send the same kind of message back to the spinal cord, then back to the fingers, and the finger muscles extend, so that the trembling is no more than a series of little finger jerks and nothing to be afraid of. Let it jerk.

MARIAN: Can you control them?

DOCTOR: Eventually, through accepting; you see, I have to teach what to do. Explanation is not always enough. I teach facing, accepting, floating, and letting time pass. Now, facing—I'll give you an example of that: a very good example of how a nervously ill man did not face what had happened. He was a Canadian and he belonged to a group of nervously ill people who were taught that to overcome the fear of going out they had to go as far as they could without panicking and then return. If he panicked, he had to return straightaway. And in this way he did get used to travelling around the village. Eventually he went to Las Vegas for a holiday, where he stayed two weeks, and he didn't panic once. He came back to Vancouver and the next day he had to go to the local bank. But when he joined the queue waiting for the bank teller and handed the same old bank book to the same teller and stood on the same spot where he had panicked so often before, he panicked again, and it was a smasher! And he thought, "What will I do now? I've had 18 months practising 'getting used to' and I've even been to America and I didn't panic, but now I'm panicking and it's worse than ever!" You see, he'd never learnt to pass through panic; had never faced the symptoms; he'd never learnt how to cope with *them*; he'd never learnt that when you panic, you let your body "flop" and are prepared to let the waves of panic sweep all over you if necessary. You see it RIGHT THROUGH. Panic is an electric flash: it's a superficial electric flash. And *that* I teach my patients: to go towards panic; to let it come; to let everything happen to the body that will with *utter acceptance*. We're changing the mood; we're reversing the pattern; from running away from fear to going into fear, losing the fear through facing the actual symptoms of fear, not by becoming used to a particular place. So that in the end, even though the panic-flash may still come—and it probably will— it no longer *matters* as much. It's the "no longer mattering" that is the key. I teach them that it's the no longer mattering that is the cure, not the actual disappearance of the symptoms. And they need to have the doctor who's going to help them with this, or my books—I hardly like to mention the books because it sounds as though

I'm trying to advertise them, actually I'm trying only to make people aware that the help is there. Help is also in the cassettes I made especially for people for the time when I myself could no longer be here. A good doctor and the books and the cassettes can help them find the courage to see the panic right through. So often, just at the very climax of panic or of other symptoms, the sufferer withdraws. And that's tension, that's more adrenalin, that's more stress hormones. And these lead to an even stronger experiencing of the symptoms. Acceptance! Let it all come, even go towards it, go out prepared to take what will come. Let one's body do what it wants to do! Don't check it, don't try not to panic; don't try to think of something else. Give in *willingly*, just as in Australia, when the big waves come we don't stand up against them, we get dumped [onto the sand] if we do; we go under them willingly. And that's accepting and facing.

MARIAN: It's almost like tranquillising yourself?

DOCTOR: Yes it is, Marian.

MARIAN: Rather than taking a tranquilliser?

DOCTOR: There is a place for tranquillisation. I know a lot has been written against tranquillisers recently. But they have their place. Some people are so sensitised that it is almost beyond their capacity to go willingly into panic, to take any of the symptoms willingly, to accept them utterly. I said "almost" beyond their capacity. There are people who will not take tranquillisers and who recover without their help; but I never ask that of my patients. Those who will, I support, and I think, "Good on you!", but those who need tranquillisation, I see that they get it *at that stage*, in two ways: first, they get enough, but not too much. I still want them to feel enough panic to know that they have to practise facing and accepting and floating and letting time pass. And secondly, there are times when they are so utterly worn out with practising that they need a rest from it for a while, and tranquillisers perhaps for just one day may give them that rest. Tranquillisation must be watched by the doctor and here "floating" is such an excellent word. You see, it implies more than just relaxation. It is relaxation with action. Consider an agoraphobic person who is afraid to enter the super-market: he can become so locked to the ground with tension he feels he cannot take another step forward, and then he usually does the very worst that he could do—he tries to force himself forward. "I will go, I'll get there, I'll get there"; but the more he forces himself, the more tension he builds up and so the more he locks himself in inaction, and the more rigid he feels he becomes. Now, if he were to let his body go utterly, and think "Float, float, don't fight! Float!", the very thought of "float" unlocks the tension of the muscles. And in that way he can float forward. He can float through a difficult situation. He can float through a situation at work, perhaps when having to confront a boss, or even through any situations that really get him down. "I'm not going to stand tensely up to this, I'm going to relax towards it, to float through it!"

MARIAN: You're saying that you can use this method for both anxiety states—the two types you talk mainly about: the one where people have got into a vicious circle, worrying about symptoms; and the second, the person who does have special problems. Can they still use that technique?

DOCTOR: Yes. Definitely. Because, first of all, the people with special problems will also eventually become afraid of their symptoms; they'll be afraid of their so-called missing heartbeats, the thumping heart, the iron-band headache, and so on. They'll be afraid of those—the symptoms of stress—while contemplating their special problem. But if they understand the symptoms; if they understand that the thumping heart is no more than the extra-strong beat of a normal heart (I'm assuming they have been examined by their doctor), that understanding takes some of the mystery, some of the bewilderment, away, so that they can then more peacefully contemplate their problem and perhaps arrive at a solution.

TALK No. 3.
NERVOUS FATIGUE

MARIAN: Fatigue can often be one of the most distressing aspects of nervous illness—tired minds can give rise to all manner of exaggerated or inappropriate thoughts. This was the problem which faced our patient, Anne.

ANNE: The nervous illness first started . . . well, the problems first started when I was 20—I'm in my thirties now. We had a burglar: I heard someone going up the stairs in the middle of the night, and it was such a shock, it scared the daylights out of me—it would scare the daylights out of anyone, I think—and the thought that we never knew who it was or heard someone coming in made it worse. After that I couldn't sleep because I was absolutely terrified and it just broke my sleep pattern, and once your sleep pattern is broken you just don't function as well. At the time I had an awful lot of stress because this was just before I got married, and I had all the arrangements to make for the wedding; I had all the trousseau to make because I'm not a stock size, so I had to make everything, and Dad was in hospital and I had to go and visit him and look after him and didn't know if the wedding was going to be on or off. And in general it was just a right old battle at that time.

Things just got worse and worse and worse. The more tired I got the more frightened I got, and the less you sleep the more tired you are. So the next morning, after no sleep, I was more tired and the next day I felt worse. Then I started getting worried about the niggly little things—had I turned the gas off properly? Better make sure! And I'd go back and back and back and I didn't know if the damn thing was on or off in the end. And I could spend hours; I just couldn't get out of the house, because I couldn't stop checking the gas cooker, and checking all the switches, et cetera.

MARIAN: Dr Weekes, what do people mean by nervous fatigue?

DOCTOR: They mean four things: muscular, emotional, mental fatigue, and a kind of fatigue of the spirit. But nervous fatigue develops so slowly, and so insidiously, that the average nervously ill person doesn't recognise its coming. And the complicated symptoms he can get, he thinks are some "strange thing" doing this to him— he doesn't realise that this is only fatigue. For example, the fact that with fatigue emotions can become so grossly exaggerated, he thinks he is going crazy—he doesn't realise that with fatigue, nerves begin to get so aroused that they register emotions so acutely, stronger, stronger, stronger! For instance, even joy can be felt almost hysterically. A sad sight can seem tragic; noise can seem overwhelming; a noisy movie can seem so insufferably noisy that the sufferer will feel like rushing out of the cinema or actually feel that he must go outside. That is very, very confusing.

MARIAN: So are people mentally ill when they reach that

stage where they're overreacting to everything?

DOCTOR: I don't think so—no. They're emotionally overreacting; it's an emotional tie-up. For instance, a nervously fatigued woman watching her mother packing to return to her own small, lonely apartment was so emotionally disturbed at the thought of her mother returning to that loneliness, she thought, "How can I go on living, feeling like this?", but that was emotional—her actual thought was all right: it was simply "My mother will be so lonely, on her own, how can I go on living feeling like this?" She didn't realise that it was she who was reacting out of all proportion; it wasn't that the situation was so terrible. One has to teach such people that it is their oversensitised reaction that is abnormal, not the situation. They should learn to understand that and learn to accept their oversensitised reaction, until with continuous acceptance their reactions gradually calm, calm, calm. But you know, while reactions are oversensitised and are so intense, they exhaust their supply of stress hormones, and the sufferer feels exhausted, and that is a type of adrenal depletion—just as when you get a person with organic adrenal disease that has not been treated (we call this Addison's Disease) those people are so tired they can hardly lift a hand. I think that's what Jane Austen had.

MARIAN: So when they're in that exhausted state, what are the first things you do to help them?

DOCTOR: Explain what's happening to them, and that it is recoverable. Instead of lying on the bed thinking, "I'll never get out of this, I can hardly lift my hand!", they must get up off that bed and start moving, even though they're exhausted. They're not going to hurt themselves by moving. It is amazing how quickly nervous exhaustion will heal if the person accepts it, accepts his jelly-legs, accepts his weakness, and works with it there; sitting down sometimes during the day and not doing unnecessary things, yes of course, but from going out and having to lean on an arm of a helper for support, within two weeks he can be walking normally if it's done with understanding and utter acceptance.

MARIAN: I imagine that some people might turn to stimulants at this time in life? They'd think, "I'll take some of those caffeine tablets, or something, just to keep me going!" I suppose, really, they shouldn't touch them at all, should they?

DOCTOR: Well, caffeine tablets will make their hearts race, too, and that's very upsetting. Stimulants—no, no, no. I never prescribe stimulants; in fact, very rarely would I prescribe tranquillisers, but, as I explained in my last talk, they have their place.

But mental fatigue does come into the picture too, and this is where a person who has brooded about his illness for a long time, gone over and over and over it, is like a student who has been studying for too long and begins to feel he can't concentrate, can't remember; also his thoughts may seem to "stick". A very tired mind seems to lose its "flexibility", and that's when a person so easily develops a phobia or an obsession. It can be as simple as that! It's simply mental fatigue working in someone with exhausting, exaggerated emotional reactions. It can be as simple as that!

MARIAN: Can nervous fatigue develop from physical fatigue? You mentioned the young student overworking. I can remember people having breakdowns when I was at college, because they seemed to be constantly working very hard over their books. That seemed to be nervous illness developing from physical stress.

DOCTOR: I think you could work as hard as you like over

your books provided you didn't become anxious because you were doing it. You'd have to add the extra stress of anxiety and fear of the exams. And finding that you were so tired, you weren't able to take the work in any longer; and then, by golly, you'd only got a fortnight, or two days or whatever it was, before the exams! Then the panic starts, and then comes the extra exhaustion of panic, the extra fear! I think that was the straw that broke the poor old student's back, not the amount of work done. You can work and work; you can become emotionally exhausted; you can become mentally exhausted, but if you don't panic because you are, if you understand what is happening and think, "Well, I'm mentally exhausted, my thoughts come haltingly, they come slowly, but if I accept this and allow time, my body will heal itself just as it'll heal a broken leg!", you'll be OK. That is the cure. Reverse the pattern, as I say all the time. Reverse the pattern with acceptance, knowing what's happening, and letting one's body heal itself, just as we let it heal a cut.

MARIAN: It's that acceptance again, isn't it, that you've been talking about in the last few talks? It's that relaxing into the situation?

DOCTOR: Yes, it's the attitude. The attitude of acceptance, based on understanding. One can even accept without understanding, and be cured. Many people who are cured through faith have done it through acceptance with faith, not on understanding. Utter acceptance can be there just on faith. But, when it's based on understanding as well, it has a stronger foundation, a much stronger foundation.

TALK NO. 4.

PHOBIAS, OBSESSIONS AND AGORAPHOBIA

MARIAN: Over the past few talks, we've built up a picture of the pattern of nervous illness. Now Dr Weekes continues her series, looking at the particular problems of phobias and obsessions—the cause of our patient Anne's nervous breakdown.

PATIENT: From time to time I used to get assessed at the hospital. They had these cards and they'd say, "Does this worry you? Does that bother you?" and one of the things on it was pins and needles and broken glass, and because broken glass was tagged on to it, I suddenly thought, "Oh, I hadn't thought of that!", and round about the same time one of the dairies was prosecuted for having, I think it was a nail, in a bottle of milk, and I suddenly thought, "What if they smashed a bottle at the milk-bottling plant! What if there is a bit of broken glass in all those milk bottles! What if they haven't checked them all carefully! And if I pour some milk into someone's drink it's going to kill them, and harm them!" So after that I had to sieve all the milk and I became so frightened, especially in relation to food, that I got to the stage where I think we lived on boiled eggs 'cause nothing much can happen to them! We got absolutely sick of boiled eggs! But I could see danger everywhere and came to be very much on my guard.

MARIAN: Dr Weekes, are phobias and obsessions the same thing?

DOCTOR: No, they're not. Not at all, but they do overlap. A phobia is a persistent, irrational fear, and obsessions are thoughts that preoccupy a mind to an abnormal degree. I don't like having to remember definitions, but there they are for you.

A phobia, although it seems a frightening thing to talk about and hear about, can be very simply developed, as you have seen in Anne. Because of that it can be very simply, to my mind, among my patients, cured. Now I didn't say "easily", I said "simply". For instance, when a phobia develops, you've had, as I've explained in the talk on nervous fatigue, the ground already prepared. You have a sensitised person whose emotions are being exaggeratedly recorded—a person who feels, instead of simply fear, a flash of panic; instead of feeling a sight is sad, feels that it is tragic. That person is in a position to get a highly sensitised reaction to what would normally be only a slightly fearful thought; and also, if he is at the same time mentally tired, he can get a sort of shock with it, so that he doesn't forget it very easily. And this is how simply a phobia can develop.

MARIAN: I was going to say, in Anne's case, it all seemed to have begun when she heard a burglar come into the house?

DOCTOR: Yes, she had a shock. But because before that she was very, very tired, the shock, as it were, brought such an intense reaction in her, she couldn't forget it. And because she was mentally tired the memory stuck and came repeatedly.

But, can I first talk about a plain phobia, a simple, uncomplicated phobia? Say, someone who has just an irrational fear of something?

There was a nervously ill nurse in a maternity hospital: let's deal with her, because her phobia is one that many nervously ill people have, that is, the fear of harming someone. She was carrying a newly born baby to have its bath and she was feeling in such a state of disintegration herself that she felt almost as if she had no control over her own thoughts and feelings. She was intensely emotional. When she looked down at the little baby that was so helpless, completely at her mercy, as it were, she suddenly had the normal thought that anybody could have, "Oh! What if I, in my present state, were to hurt that baby, harm that baby accidentally?", and then, because she was so sensitised, that thought soon became, "Oh, what if I hurt it *on purpose*?" Such an easy transition! And at the time she happened to be standing beside an open window and then, quick as a flash, came the thought, "What if I were to throw it out on purpose?" So she rushed past the window and whenever she came along that corridor with a baby—and she had to carry them throughout the day—she hurried past that particular window. From then on windows brought back the fear, so that she became afraid to pass almost any window. She always got that "whoosh" of fear in the stomach.

She went to a therapist for help and he told her, "You are an aggressive type; there is this hidden aggression." Well, of course that made her feel guilty, so now windows meant guilt. The phobia was compounding, it was building up, and I was able to show her how normal the situation had been at the beginning: her reaction was normal in the circumstances of her sensitisation; with her feeling that she wasn't secure within herself, how could she give security to a little one?—that's normal. And isn't it normal to suddenly think, "If I might accidentally hurt . . ." and then to think, "What if I did hurt . . .?" That is how so many mothers, if they're listening to me today, have felt this about children. They're not aggressive types; they're only very tired, vulnerable people; and that is only a thought that they think, it has no substance at all. Such people would never hurt their children.

MARIAN: So when they think that thought, what else should they think?

DOCTOR: They do what I taught Anne to do: to understand that it is only a strange thought in a very tired mind, and they don't try to stop it coming. Because that only underlines the trouble in red. They accept the thought; they will think the thought, because it's been their habit to think that thought; but they must see it for what it is: only a strange, frightening thought in a very tired mind. They're not aggressive people, they are normal, caring people, but very vulnerable.

MARIAN: They're often, it seems to me, very courageous people too, in the struggle they often go through to try to come out of this nervous period of their life. In fact, I remember reading in one of your books that you say that one of the friends that they need is the friend Courage.

DOCTOR: Strangely enough, I have found that my nervously ill patients are among the bravest people I have ever known—because they have to get themselves better from a state where they're practically on the floor with suffering, with very little help except the right inner voice within themselves. You know, some people envy people who, they think, are confident, but very often the person who appears confident is only self-assertive. True confidence has to be earned, and it's a wonderful opportunity to have none, because you can start from rock bottom and get it! And these nervously ill people, they get it. And when they are better, if they have got better the right way on their own effort, they will be really integrated people.

Now, Anne, as I explained, was to me not only one

of the bravest but one of the most intelligent people that I've ever known, and to go on this program, the way she has, shows great courage. And I hope that her friends and neighbours appreciate that. I hope the whole district is proud of Anne, to think that she was willing to expose herself in this way, for the sake of helping other people. She's a great lass, Anne.

So that courage has to be there; but with Anne it wasn't just a question of teaching her to know that her obsessions were just strange thoughts in a tired mind: Anne had to first glimpse the truth and then practise holding that glimpse for longer and longer. An obsessive person can't say, "Well, yes, you've explained it to me, Doctor, I understand", and walk out of the surgery cured. Usually the minute they leave the surgery the obsession will slap them in the face again, and their body will react in exactly the same emotional way that is usual, and they will think, "I'm lost—she's told me all about it, but I'm still doing it!"

So they must practise glimpsing often and regularly, especially when they have the obsessive thought, which is wrongly directed thought, and which feels almost as if it is compelling them, perhaps even propelling them into action. That's when they must especially practise glimpsing, that it is only a strange thought in a tired mind, and for a moment, perhaps just for a second, they will hold the truth and will not feel that overwhelming wave of compulsion. There can be a little peace, perhaps just for a moment. That's what they build on, that fleeting feeling of peace; that's what Anne built on. It's a long, long way they have yet to go, a lot of glimpsing yet to do, but the answer is cure, as it was with Anne.

MARIAN: Dr Weekes, there is one question I would like to put to you, because throughout this conversation you haven't mentioned agoraphobia. Now is that because the problem is a different problem from other phobias? Or is it because the treatment is different?

DOCTOR: The treatment is much the same. Agoraphobia does differ from other phobias: in my opinion it is not a true phobia. It means fear of the open fields [literally, from the ancient Greek, fear of the marketplace], and there are people who are afraid of that, but who are not afraid of going anywhere else. These are true agoraphobics. However, today we use the term "agoraphobic" to embrace people who are afraid of leaving home, for fear they will have a "turn". They are afraid, not of the outside surroundings per se, but of themselves. Will they panic? Will they collapse? What will they *do* in a situation? It's not so much that they are afraid of the school meeting, or the hairdresser, but afraid that if clamped in the hairdresser's chair they won't be able to get out quickly enough if they have a panic. And the treatment is *always the same: utter acceptance, even of panic*. They have to learn how to take the panic: take a deep breath and let it out quickly, and as the breath is let out, let the body slump and let the panic flash. It is only an electric discharge. They must not let their life be ruined by an electric discharge. They must see it right through. And because they're sensitised, it may linger on for a while, but what the heck, if it does? I know that it can be so strong that they think it's impossible, impossible to bear. It is never impossible to bear, and it's only by going through that last one per cent of the flash with utter acceptance that they discover this. It's when they withdraw just as they think it's getting impossible, when they shrink before it, that they make it seem more impossible and are defeated by it. But if they are prepared to see it right through, they find peace on the other side of panic. They went through it! They know it! They've done it! That is the way for them to cope with agoraphobia. No fighting! All acceptance! To my mind it is the only way.

TALK NO. 5.

DEPRESSION

MARIAN: Depression can be one of the most self-defeating obstacles to recovering from nervous illness. Dr Weekes has treated many patients for depression, and has developed special insight into how to offset some of its alarming symptoms.

DOCTOR: I found that in my practice, depressed people fitted into two main groups: there were the people who were not nervously ill but who suffered from recurring bouts of depression; and then there were the people who, as a result of the emotional and mental fatigue in nervous illness, finally became apathetic and then deeply depressed. In my practice there were these two main types.

Now first consider the person with recurring bouts of depression. She, or he, invariably goes about curing herself, or himself, the wrong way. Take a housewife (we'll forget the men for the moment) who stands at the window, at dusk, looking out wearily. She has had bouts of depression before, and there's just something about the dusk, perhaps a distant church bell or something, that strikes a sinking note inside her and she feels her heart, as she says, go "Whoooff", and she feels that clutching hand on her tummy. She thinks, "Oh no! Not one of my bouts again!" Now, if she's busy, and if she has the supper to get, and if she goes ahead and does it, the chances are she'll forget about the approaching depression, but if she has another one of those sinking feelings, then she'll think, "It's coming! One of my bouts is coming!" She becomes immediately apprehensive and afraid, because she knows what they're like; she knows what it's like to go through a bout of depression. And now—this is where she does the wrong thing—she starts to rush here and rush there, to try to get rid of it. She'll rush to the supermarket, and when she's finished she'll think, "Has it gone? Am I better? Has it really gone?", and of course the best way to remember something is to try too hard to forget it. And with this added anxiety and fear of a bout coming, and rushing around, she becomes very tired, depleted, and of course that helps her to become more depressed. And so, a bout of depression soon begins.

Of course, the family say, "Oh, Mum, get yourself up out of this one, for goodness' sake. Do something about this one!" She's been doing this perhaps for days, has been trying to get herself up and out of it; but the more she tries the deeper she gets into it.

This is a perfect example of how not to manage a bout of depression. The way to manage it is: when she thinks that she's feeling a bout of depression coming, she should let it come and not rush anywhere, she should work at a steady pace with the feeling of depression there. That's the secret. She should let the feeling be there, face it, have it. It is temporary depletion on her part: some little thing, perhaps some thought, some memory, has started it; she's perhaps been overtired. She should *work with it there*, relax towards depression, take it with her, not try to lose it, not try to run away from it, not try to fight it. And while she relaxes in her thought towards it, her body will relax, and her emotional battery will recharge itself, because she's not discharging it all day with fear and with rushing here and rushing there, and so adding more and more tension. But very few people do that: they usually do rush and they are tense and they do add fear.

I have not talked very much about the person who becomes depressed as a result of a nervous illness: that second type. It is important to recognise that when someone becomes depressed as a result of nervous illness, recovery usually takes more time, because they are usually so physically depleted, and this is where a family, if they can only understand, can help. Instead they usually try to help with false cheer, such as saying, "Mum, come and have a game of cards with the Johnsons. It'll do you good!" So poor old Mum gets up her courage and plays cards with the Johnsons, and if she doesn't come home any better, they think despairingly, "Oh, Mum'll never get better! We thought she'd enjoy it." Mum gets more upset because she's even more tired after her effort to play cards with the Johnsons, so she's perhaps more depressed. That is nervous depletion, and it takes time to heal. Such people have to realise that when they have been nervously ill and have become apathetic and depressed, they have adrenal glands to replenish. A game of cards with the Johnsons alone won't do it. However, she should still go out and sometimes even play cards with the neighbours. She should accept invitations and do what she has to do within reason, but not force herself too much, always realising that there is a depletion to be healed, food to be eaten, perhaps vitamins to take, sleep to get and above all, depletion to be healed—gently.

TALK No. 6.

SETBACKS ON THE WAY TO RECOVERY

MARIAN: In the last of Dr Weekes's talks, we turn now to the road to recovery from nervous illness, a road which, though simple, is not always as straightforward as it seems. I asked Dr Weekes about the setbacks which can delay the process of recovery.

DOCTOR: One of the bogeymen that hide in the woodpile is memory, and it's always there to bluff and persuade the person trying to get better, that he won't get better, or that he's not getting better. "You see," one woman said, "I can get the children off to school in the morning, but it's afterwards when I'm over the sink that I go all weak and giddy." It's the memory of all the other mornings when she has stood at the sink and gone "all weak and giddy" that makes her feel weak and giddy again. What actually happens is simply that her very apprehension stimulates production of more stress hormone than is usual; stress hormone (adrenalin) dilates the blood vessels in the muscles of her legs and the blood pools down into her legs, naturally leaving the top part of her body with less blood, so that she feels faint and wobbly. She's done it to herself, but she doesn't know that. Memory is the old trickster that says "You'll feel weak at the sink, you know. You felt weak and wobbly at the sink all those other days!"

Memory works in another peculiar way. It works immediately and it works at a distance; there are these two kinds. Now, memory working immediately: a person who is feeling depressed and who perhaps is tired of fighting to try and get better, will suddenly feel not too bad. He's played a game of tennis, and he's talked to people, he's been to a theatre, he's lost himself in watching a play, and suddenly, when it's over, memory strikes and he thinks, "No, you're not like them, you're in a breakdown!", and a wave of apprehension and despair will sweep over him. I call this "flashback memory", and he's got to learn to pass on, on and through, always on; and not to let memory try to hold him back, try to draw him back.

Also, there's the other person who goes away for a holiday and is fine while he's away: goes into cafés, goes on buses, does things he perhaps hasn't done for ages, but as soon as he sees home, the same rooms, the same houses, the same shops, memory smites: memory and sight, memory and sound, memory and smells! And not only that; because he has suffered the symptoms of nervous illness, memory may bring feelings back: it may not just be thought that comes back, it's thought and feeling. And the feeling can still be very acute, because of what he's been through. Memory knows the way to bring back so much feeling, not only perhaps the trembling hands, the apprehension, but the whole orchestra: the headache, the tummy, everything.

MARIAN: How does he handle a setback like that? Or don't you consider that to be a setback?

DOCTOR: No. Oddly enough, I teach my patients that a setback can be a chance for a step forward. I like them, and I like it when patients have a setback, to think, "Well, this is what Dr Weekes likes, because it'll give me another chance to practise what I have to do!" You see, in between setbacks, they gather hope and they have a rest from their suffering. However, they learn more in a setback. A setback faced the right way is more experience, brings more confidence. Also, by coming through setbacks the sufferer is able to build up a stronger and stronger inner voice. An inner voice that says

"You've been there before, old chap, you know the way. On! Forward! Don't go back, go *through*!" That inner voice is what will support and direct.

To me that's the beginning of recovery, and it can only be there if it's been earned by facing, accepting, floating, and letting time pass. And that takes time, and time may mean many setbacks. So many, that the sufferer knows the way out so well that he no longer fears the way in! You hear some therapists say, "There's no such thing as recovery", as one said to me on television in New York. She said "Dr Weekes, we do not speak of recovering from nervous illness, we speak only of remission!" So I said to her, "I've treated so many patients and I've seen so many recover, that I'm not afraid to talk of nervously ill people recovering". But to me a recovery does not mean having no nervous symptoms again. We all have stressful symptoms as long as we live, and recovery means knowing how to accept them and go through them and cope with them, so that they no longer matter. No longer mattering is the key and recognising the importance of developing the right inner voice can so often be missed by therapists. You see, there are many ways of treating nervous illness, and when I spoke to psychiatrists and psychologists at White Plains Hospital in New York this year, I knew that some of them would, of course, treat their patients differently from me and that they had great faith in their methods. The last thing I wanted to do was to criticise anybody's method. Provided they cure by it, it's a good method. But in the talk I gave I stressed that whatever the method, the one goal that we must all have is for the patient to develop the *right* inner voice.

A woman journalist, an Englishwoman, wrote an article for a magazine about four years ago and she said, "I've been agoraphobic for two years. I can now go anywhere, provided I take these three little pills, one three times a day." It was a certain pill: the other kinds didn't suit her, but this particular pill did. She said, "I can go anywhere and all I have to do now is to come off the little pill!" (I notice she wrote the article before she tried to come off the little pill.) She might be all right too, provided the day she came off the little pills she said to herself, "Well, you don't need any more pills, you can go here, you can go there, you can do everything. You're all right, no more pills, you won't need them!" She'd be all right . . . temporarily. I say "temporarily" because if she were to meet the same stress in the future that had originally caused her agoraphobia, what would she do? She had no right inner voice to tell her. She would think, "Where are my pills?" And what then, if a voice within herself said, "Oh, girl, you're depending on pills! Suppose these pills don't do the trick this time?" Where is she then? An inner voice, the right inner voice, should be the goal of every therapist: he should see that his patients develop the right inner voice through having made their own successful effort; that, having failed, they've practised again and again until finally they have learnt that they themselves can take themselves by the hand through any experience by facing and accepting—utter, utter acceptance—by floating and waiting until the symptoms lighten and finally no longer matter.

MARIAN: Throughout our talks, you've implied that much of the improvement that you can make finally comes through self help, but how much support do we need from the family, from the doctor?

DOCTOR: Marian, many, many people have had to recover with no support from either family or doctor, and they do it. But if they can have support, that is fantastic. You see, Anne has had wonderful support from her husband, and I'm sure that has made all the difference in the world to Anne.

MARIAN: Yes, because we have over the weeks seen how Anne has struggled. She struggled over many years. She went through many, many different types of treatment before your words helped her. It seems that the right words at the right time can obviously help a great number of people.

DOCTOR: Oh, you've no conception of how important your statement is. As the right words at the right time help, so the wrong words at the wrong time condemn to a life of misery. And that's why doctors should be so careful of what they say. People take a doctor's words so seriously. I think for a doctor to do as little harm as possible with his words is so important. And I think that's how I helped with Anne. I really showed her by using the right words just when she needed them most.

MARIAN: Dr Weekes, thank you very much indeed for all the help you've given us over the weeks, and thanks not only from me but from Anne too. And I think it would be very apt indeed to end with a little bit of our film of Anne and you can see just how well she is now.

DOCTOR: Thank you, Marian.

ANNE: When you've been as ill as I was—and an obsessional illness is one of the nastiest things in the book—and I've had it, and I've had it in good measure, and I've had it for a long time, and I've had every treatment there is, and I've had a lot of experiments done. And when you've had that sort of illness, that sort of background, and you're better, and you get over it, you take delight in just being alive—just peace in your head.

If anyone were to ask me if I'm happy now I'd say "Oh yes!" You know, it's only with everyday things that everyone takes for granted: just being with my family and having us all safe and well and a happy marriage. It's things that people say may be a bit humdrum. But if you've not been in hell, you don't know what heaven is, you know. And it's absolutely super. So I can truly say that I'm happy!

3

The Maintenance of Peace

After I gave those six BBC talks I returned home to Australia almost immediately, where I remained. I often thought of the people in Britain using my teaching. Some wrote saying how well they were; one woman wrote "Thank you for a life restored!", so I knew that at least they were happy.

I also knew that although the guidelines I taught brought recovery if followed, there were certain obstacles to recovery that were predictable, even bewildering, and yet could be so simply explained. Knowing that many people in Britain were now at the stage where they probably needed such explanation, and wanting so much to give it to them, in July 1985, despite my age and home commitments, I flew to London to go on television once more.

In London, on television, I not only stressed how to negotiate the way to recovery to finally find peace, but how to maintain that peace, having found it.

This chapter is that last interview.

MARIAN: Now, Dr Weekes, we will talk about the maintenance of peace. Let me ask you first of all, what is a setback?

DOCTOR: It's a halting place in recovery, Marian. It's part of recovery, and to me it's not a setback: it's just another chance to practise what the nervously ill person knows will help them—it's important in recovery.

MARIAN: Because, for a lot of people, it must be very distressing to have actually recovered, not just for days but perhaps for weeks, and then to find they're going right back again into the symptoms of nervousness, the palpitations, et cetera. It must be a very depressing moment in their lives?

DOCTOR: Marian, on the way to recovery, or once a person thinks he or she has recovered, there's still a very close alliance between what they think and what they feel and from what they *think* they can get this flashing, intense, emotional reaction. That is there for a long time, it is there underneath, even if life goes on peacefully for them; they don't necessarily *feel* it, but during the recovery, and even after recovery, it is very often still there. Now that can bring certain shocks and these shocks, while they are not difficult for the person who understands them to pass through, they are very upsetting for the person who doesn't understand them. Take a man, for instance, who has gone to the theatre, has enjoyed the play, loses himself in it and feels normal, like the others. Then the lights go on, he stands up, and suddenly realisation of what he's still going through smites him and he thinks, "Yes, but you're not like the others! You've got this 'thing'! You're still ill." And then "Whoosh!!!", fear hits him; his emotional reaction is so intense. The contrast between the peace he's just had in the theatre and the suffering he had only a few hours ago is too great. He despairs. How can he ever get better? That's a big hurdle. The world seems so unreal, so strange, that he would rather be back in his illness.

It feels more real; he knows where he is there. Furthermore, there's the shock involved. One man in Fiji had played tennis all the afternoon, and swum; indeed he'd had a peaceful night, had wakened peacefully and had thought, "This is wonderful—if I go back to work, I'll be all right!" Then he made a very quick turn in his room to open the window and had a dizzy spell. Now, he had had dizzy spells before during his illness, and immediately he felt back in his illness . . . you see, the shock of the dizzy spell brought back symptoms of shock: the trembling, the whole works, et cetera.

MARIAN: So what should he have done?

DOCTOR: He has to go through these shocks. He must pass on, always through! Waking in the morning is another shock, the shock of just waking can bring a quickly beating heart and a feeling of foreboding—the nervously ill person feels almost balanced on a razor's edge. But what he feels like in the morning is not necessarily what he will feel like for the rest of the day. It's not a prediction of the day to come: it's a hangover from the suffering of the days and the weeks beforehand.

Then there's another shock—a very important one: goofy thoughts. As one American said, "You wouldn't know, Doctor, the goofy thoughts I think." They think not only goofy thoughts, but thoughts they would never normally dream of thinking. Nervously fatigued nuns will come to me complaining of thoughts they think in church, and they say it's the Devil tempting them and they then think they must surely fight these thoughts, that they must not have them. Some think they are even going mad. These are all hurdles to real recovery, Marian.

MARIAN: How can they cope with these?

DOCTOR: I'll tell you what they must do: they must accept all shocks, no matter what, as part of their normal living.

It doesn't matter what they think, they must not be afraid to think, however bizarre the thoughts seem. It's not as if they have to use only one part of their brain and avoid the rest!

The same thing happens with what I call the very last hurdle of all: for example, I had a telephone call from America yesterday and the caller, a man, said, "I'm 99 per cent cured, but my last one per cent is that I can't get over the hurdle of being so much aware of myself." Of course a person who's been nervously ill may be unduly aware of themselves! They've been aware of themselves for weeks, months, even years; they can't lose the habit in a day; they can't say, "Now, I must not be so aware of myself!" It will take time for self-awareness to fade, of course it must! So they must treat all their funny thoughts, even if terrible thoughts, as part of their ordinary thinking. Not treat it any differently from ordinary thinking. Even as shocks come they must think "I will pass through these shocks; I must go on with what I'm doing; no going back, no being pushed back by these shocks!" Never be set back by shock, no matter what it is. On, always on! If aware of yourself, be aware of yourself, what the heck!

Unfortunately, some therapists will try to help their patients by saying "Think of something else, old man! Get your mind on to other thoughts!", but very few people are successful in trying to get rid of thoughts on order, very few can get rid of unwanted thoughts like that. They should think of whatever their mind brings them: always go with it, let the thoughts come, whatever they are.

MARIAN: Is that the time for that inner voice to come? The voice you talk about so much? How can it come to your aid?

DOCTOR: It's a cushion, Marian. However, it must be earned by the sufferer himself, by his efforts in facing, accepting, floating (not fighting) and letting time pass. When he's done it that way, if he's failed and still come out of the failure again and again and again successfully, he strengthens that inner voice; the support of the right inner voice is his crutch. That is his salvation. Tranquillisers will help, but they will never, ever cure.

MARIAN: Are you saying that there are times when someone could use tranquillisers?

DOCTOR: Definitely. Too much has been written inadvisedly about tranquillisers by people who've never had the experience of using them on patients.

MARIAN: But there are dangers, aren't there?

DOCTOR: Definitely. But not when properly used; when prescribed by a doctor who is willing to see his patient right through their use and not just to let his secretary hand prescriptions across her desk. A doctor who uses them intelligently, for example, knows that there are times when a few days' tranquillisation will help an exhausted patient; or revive his spirits if they're flagging. Tranquillisers have an important use. Not everybody will take them and not everybody needs them. You can go through the greatest panic, you can go through the worst symptoms, without tranquillisers; but many people think they do need them and they should be given them intelligently and withdrawn from them intelligently.

One thing I would like to say—and it struck me while I was reading Vera Brittain's book *Testament of Youth*: she related what a Dutchman had said to her when she had remarked on how, after the last war, the Dutch that she was meeting in Holland seemed quiet but not exactly at peace. The Dutchman had said to Vera Brittain then, "You must give us time to grow into peace." I would like nervously ill people to think of that Dutchman, and remember that there is no switch to turn the suffering off; there's no instant balm for peace and comfort. Time is the healer, but with the right approach, Marian. And it is so important for people never to lose hope.

MARIAN: Let me say that somehow or other you have found the time, since I met you a couple of years ago, to write another book. It's called *More Help for Your Nerves* and in fact it covers many of the sorts of questions that viewers at home have asked you, written to you about, since you were here last. There was one question that I found very interesting: how does a person know when they're cured?

DOCTOR: When they cope with themselves and especially can cope with whatever reaction they have. It's not that they must have no reaction, but that they know how to cope with the reactions that come. Cure has to include remembrance of the experience of the illness, not forgetting it. The sufferer is cured when he can take the memory of his illness and with it any symptoms that return, because they *no longer matter*. No longer mattering is recovery—that is the cure. Of course memory will return, but it doesn't mean the illness has returned. We can only forget when we are sound asleep or anaesthetised.

MARIAN: Well, Dr Weekes, thank you very much, we would like to end on that positive note, and I look forward to seeing you again on your next visit to England.

DOCTOR: Thank you, Marian.

4

Interview for Radio, 1983

The day that I finished the last of my interviews on BBC television (presented in Chapter Two), Marian Foster and I made this interview for radio. So, there will be some repetition of the work given in the television series; however, since this book is published as treatment for nervous people as well as entertainment, I believe the repetition will be welcomed by these people. When I remember the many times I've had to repeat myself when treating such patients in the past, I make no excuse for repetition. I want the message in this work to be so familiar that it comes unbidden, almost automatically, when needed.

MARIAN: Dr Weekes, you've helped so many nervously ill people over the years, and yet I believe you actually started your Medicine as a general practitioner.

DOCTOR: That's right.

MARIAN: How did this vast knowledge of yours, this understanding of agoraphobia and nervous illness, begin?

DOCTOR: Several ways. When I was in my late twenties, that was before I was a medical doctor, I was sent away to the country with what they thought was TB, and

I was told that for six months I must make no effort, not even to pull a blind down. I was more or less confined to lying on the couch, with nothing much to do, and six months on my hands. So that I knew what it was to become introverted, worried. That was way back in the 1920s, and I was not X-rayed. Of course, I believed I had TB, which, to a healthy young girl, was something to have to get used to. And I remember, when I left the mountains—I'd stayed in the mountains where a lot of patients who had TB were sent—I went to stay in the country with a friend, who was married to a doctor. I can remember, I'd lost all confidence in what I could do, because I'd been told "You mustn't do this, you mustn't do that!" I remember walking out alone and thinking "I wonder if I can walk as far as the corner of that street?" I remember being aware of every footstep I took, and wondering how much faith I could still have in my body to get there. I'm sure I didn't panic, only because it didn't enter my head to panic, that was all. Had I panicked then, I could have gone on to being agoraphobic, I'm sure of that. This is why I have a sympathy for agoraphobic people. I remember also that by that time my heart would palpitate if I woke up at night, just the shock of waking would make it accelerate.

I was staying with this friend who was married to the doctor. I remember very clearly how, one night, I called out to her when my heart was beating fiercely and I thought my last gasp was coming. Her husband, the doctor, said, "No, I won't go and help her. She'll think she's worse than she really is!" But one word from him then, about sensitisation and how it was "only my nerves" being sensitised, would have saved me two years of worry and suffering. However, perhaps it was just as well because what I learnt then has helped me help hundreds of thousands of people. Perhaps I should thank the doctor. However, while I suffered, I still worked. I submitted my thesis for my Doctorate of Science and got it; I can remember that while working, my heart would bang heavily against my typewriter if I leant against it; but I still worked, I still did the thesis.

In 1929 I sailed from Sydney to England—to the University of London—still with palpitations! Actually, the journey by ship was wonderful because the rhythm and the vibrations of the ship saved me from noticing the vibrations of my own body. However, when I arrived in London the sudden quietness after being on board ship meant that I was once more listening in to my own body. I was afraid of my reactions, frightened by them, worried by them, so I didn't want to be alone in the quietness. I wanted to be always with people.

I remember that my laboratory was on the top floor of University College and a friend of mine, who'd been in the Army during the First World War, flew up the stairs to greet me. I met him with "Oh, John, I can't take this any longer, I've had it!" He said, "What's wrong?" I told him what I was going through. "Oh," he said, and he just shrugged. "That's nothing, those are only the symptoms of nerves—we all had those in the trenches," and he explained to me that what I had been so worried about were only the symptoms of fear— my own fear. "That makes sense!" I said, "All this time I've been doing this to myself?" He said, "Yes" and laughed. Within a month I was cured, and climbing mountains in Switzerland. So you see, I know how important symptoms can be. I had everything to live for, and I knew it—I'd achieved so much, the whole of life lay before me, but I was incapacitated by the symptoms of fear and had never been told that that was all they were. I had been to doctors, specialists, and yet nobody had mentioned the symptoms of fear—and the symptoms of fear had been so fearful!

While I was ill in London, at night I'd just be going off to sleep when I'd suddenly wake with a start and a racing heart, which quickly became palpitations. And then I'd sit up for hours for fear that I'd die if I lay down. But after my friend told me the cause, I'd just lie and think, as calmly as I could, "OK, I'll go to sleep palpitating if necessary!", and I did, and soon the whole thing cleared up. So later when I became a medical practitioner and went into general practice, I became very sympathetic towards patients who came to me in an anxiety state, because I knew what it was like to be in one.

MARIAN: Just out of interest, was it TB that you had?

DOCTOR: No, it wasn't. I was X-rayed later. That was a misdiagnosis; I'd had severely infected tonsils and I'd eaten very little for months. I'd lost two stone.

MARIAN: Are you saying, once you became a GP you had that natural understanding of what so many of your patients were going through?

DOCTOR: Oh yes, I got a name for being interested in nervously ill people, so that people would come to me from various parts of Australia. Australia is a very big place; they'd come thousands of miles—from Perth to Sydney—and I had some of them staying in my home, perhaps three or four at a time. It was very difficult for them, staying in a guesthouse, because they wouldn't know what to do with themselves all day; my mother said, "Why don't we have them stay here?" I think I explained to you earlier, over our talks on the BBC, that we had nervously ill people staying at my home and in that way I really got to know quite a bit about their suffering. I wasn't actually interested in agoraphobia at that time, because to me, agoraphobia was, and still is, only one stage in an anxiety state. I was more interested in people in the whole anxiety state.

I remember one girl, she'd come down from the north, from Newcastle, and when she was cured she said, "I'm called 'the psychiatrist of Newcastle' now, people are coming to me to be cured, and I'm not even a doctor!"

MARIAN: You're using the word "cured"?

DOCTOR: Yes, Marian.

MARIAN: You're actually saying that people can be cured?

DOCTOR: Of course, I have no fear of using the word "cured". I get a little sad when I hear some therapists saying that nervous illness can't be cured, only relieved. You see, it can be cured as long as the person who has suffered is prepared to live with the memory of that suffering, and knows how to cope with its recurrences. We can't obliterate memory. So if memory brings the feelings back, the feelings of suffering, the sufferer may feel sure he's sick again and his therapist will often agree and tell him that he's not yet cured and that obviously they haven't got to the real cause of it. Now, if you lose someone you love (perhaps they die), you often suffer when you think of them. But in spite of this, most of us are prepared to go on living without them. We can't say to our heart "Don't suffer!" We have to live with the feelings in our heart, and despite the aching, we do live on. However, the person who's had a nervous illness, and is now cured, can't say to himself "You must never suffer again," especially when he remembers his past suffering! Of course he will remember his suffering, but that doesn't mean he is not cured. That means only that memory is up to its old tricks.

MARIAN: But I wonder . . . surely there must be some sorts of mental conditions that can't be cured? When you're speaking specifically about nervous illness, what do you mean? What sort of illness?

DOCTOR: I mean the anxiety state, and that covers the presence of crippling anxiety, perhaps accompanied by phobias and obsessions. These can be cured.

MARIAN: I know that you focus a lot, too, on the role of fatigue?

DOCTOR: Yes.

MARIAN: You talk about different types of fatigue, from physical to spiritual. Explain a little more about what you mean by "fatigue".

DOCTOR: Nervous fatigue comes as a reaction to continuous stress, and when we are under constant stress, we react in four main ways: there is muscular fatigue, emotional fatigue, mental fatigue and spiritual fatigue. I think that about covers the main ingredients of nervous fatigue.

Muscular fatigue we all know, but there are two main kinds of muscular fatigue. First, there is the muscular fatigue that we get after we've climbed Mount Everest—you know that one, don't you? When you come home after the effort and lie in a lovely hot bath and think "I've climbed Mount Everest!" This is a beautiful feeling and that's good; that's pure muscular fatigue, and we luxuriate in it. However, the muscular fatigue that comes with nervous fatigue is quite different. It means that muscles have been under too much tension for too long. You see, our muscles are never completely relaxed, they're in "tone". If a muscle were completely relaxed, we couldn't do much with it; it has to be in tone, ready for movement; which means that there are usually two sets of muscles concerned with one action, one antagonising the other, balancing to keep it in check.

When you see a pianist put his or her arms on the keyboard ready to play, if their muscles are in perfect balance (in tone), they're going to produce the best sound from that piano. And this is how we function normally. However, if we're under a lot of stress, one set of muscles may become more tensed than the other, and if muscles are like this—constantly contracted, tensed—they become fatigued, and this is what I mean by nervous fatigue in muscles. The person who is tensed like this may find that his neck muscles get tired or stiff because neck muscles are so easily constantly tensed.

Emotional fatigue is also important, because nerves under stress usually react more and more intensely as time goes on. If emotions could make a noise, then when under constant stress, the noise would get louder and louder and louder. To put it another way, reverberating circuits bring a heightened response. I call this "becoming sensitised". For instance, suppose you're in a room trying to concentrate and someone outside is making a distressing noise. At first you may hardly notice it, but after a while—if you're unduly tense—you really take notice and start listening. It might only be a ticking clock or somebody doing something quite simple, but it seems to get louder and louder, until it becomes a very loud noise indeed. For example, noise at the movies can become almost intolerable. This is why some people have to rush outside—their nerves have become "aroused" to record sensation and emotion very intensely; also, what may normally be just sad seems tragic, and what may be only a happy moment may become almost hysterical. One nervously ill person, staying with a friend, sang one of Schubert's songs with such spirit, her friend turned and said "Oh, there's nothing wrong with you; you're not as depressed as you thought you were, you couldn't have sung better!", but that singing had been almost hysterical, because the relief of finding herself actually singing had made her happiness become exaggerated into hysteria. When emotionally fatigued, emotions can swing up too high one minute and down into a depression the next. That can be so bewildering to the nervously ill person; it's hard for the sufferer to understand it.

MARIAN: Is it different from mental fatigue?

DOCTOR: Very different. A person who is emotionally fatigued can feel so unbalanced, he thinks he is going mad; even the slightest strain may seem almost unbearable for him. Once when in the outpatients department, a young student suffering from nervous illness said to me, "I think I'll have to give up Medicine!" I asked why and he answered "You see that old woman over there? All she's got is bronchitis, yet the strain of just hearing her cough makes me feel as if she's dying! I wasn't like that before; what's happening to me?" I explained that he had become so sensitised by his own suffering that his reaction to hearing her cough had become so magnified, it felt tragic.

When people are sensitised like that, they become so frightened of the state they are in, so bewildered by it, that they think of little else. And if they think, think, think, like this with *anxiety*, they become very tired mentally; you can think all day if you don't think anxiously; it's the anxiety that brings the tension and so the mental fatigue. When a student studies, he may study with anxiety, because exams may be just around the corner: if so, he may get early brain-fag; then if he's wise he'll push aside his books and go outside and hose his garden for a while—at least until he feels better— then come back later to study again. However, when a nervously ill person goes out to hose his garden, he's sure to take himself and his worries with him. He thinks anxiously about himself all the time, so that his mind gets no rest. He may become agitated, with racing thoughts, or perhaps, instead of their racing, his thoughts may become so slowed his thinking may seem retarded, and he may even stutter when he tries to speak. If he's like this, and at the same time so sensitised that he's getting an exaggerated reaction to any emotion, he has only to come up against a problem for it to seem tremendous and difficult to discard.

For instance, one woman was having her hair dyed— in those days they used the indelible lead pencil (I think it was called "indelible")—and the hairdresser happened to say "I hope you haven't got any sores on your head, because if you have, you could get poisoned with this dye!" Now that woman was already going through a mentally and emotionally exhausting time, so she couldn't get that suggestion from her mind. When she came to me for help a few months later, she said "Everywhere I look, everything I do, I think I'm getting poisoned!" She couldn't throw the thought off. A mentally tired mind acts just as if it's sticky: anxious thoughts cling, so that some people seem to have one or more anxious thoughts going around and around in their head. I can remember having brain fag after my final exams—we did more than 20 exams in one month, that's a marathon, you know—and I was 42, quite an age for final medical exams; also I'd had major surgery the week after they finished. Of course I had complications, so instead of going immediately to work as an intern in a hospital, the superintendent of the hospital agreed that I should have a month's holiday. I stayed with a friend in another State. I can remember how, in the aeroplane, I couldn't get a certain tune off my mind. It was "La Ronde": quite a tricky tune to have going over and over in one's mind! Luckily I was wise enough to let it keep going. I sang "La Ronde" all the way from Sydney to Melbourne, and I didn't try to stop myself. This is where obsessions can begin and where so many make the mistake of trying to force a tired mind from going on and on and worrying about it.

There's a group in Australia that advises members to try to crowd out unwelcome thoughts by thinking other thoughts. In my opinion that rarely works. The more you try to direct your mind not to think certain thoughts, the more it'll want to think them. So I sang "La Ronde" willingly until my interest wandered and my mind itself decided to stop.

MARIAN: What if they're not very nice thoughts?

DOCTOR: That doesn't matter either. One American man said "I think such goofy thoughts, Doctor!"

MARIAN: Perhaps even violent thoughts?

DOCTOR: Yes, of course. They very often will be thoughts that will hold fear; and violent thoughts can certainly hold fear. They're not always as innocent as "La Ronde". A person who is mentally tired easily has recurring, "sticky" thoughts. The recurrence alone can frighten, bewilder him, and because he becomes bewildered, he may even think that he's going mad. The more he thinks like this, the more the tension and fear mount. It's almost as if there's some force outside himself, or even—what seems worse—within himself, pushing him into these thoughts. Let them push him! They don't matter. They're only thoughts in a very tired mind, in a very tense, frightened person. He must not make the mistake of thinking "I mustn't think of that!" and then try to avoid it. He should think of anything, *willingly*, and if it's goofy, make it even goofier; make it more frightening. What does it matter? *They are only thoughts!* When people understand nervous fatigue this way, especially understand mental fatigue in this way, and are no longer frightened by it, that is the first step to recovery. It's just as if they are two people: one is the nervously exhausted body, and the other looks down on it and lets it bring what it wants to bring and knows that whatever it brings no longer matters. Not mattering is, of course, the key to recovery. All the upsetting happenings with the right treatment—and that includes full understanding—no longer matter. So many sufferers, even so many therapists, make the mistake of thinking that the sufferer can find peace only by getting rid of all the symptoms. Sure, you get rid of the symptoms eventually, not by their sudden absence, but by their presence coming to no longer matter; to no longer matter whether they are there or not.

MARIAN: What about spiritual fatigue? Do you mean there are people lacking in religious belief, so that they're living in a sort of vacuum? What exactly is spiritual fatigue?

DOCTOR: Religion has nothing to do with my meaning of spiritual fatigue. I mean: the sufferer comes to what he thinks is a dead end; he's made such momentous effort for so long, he feels not only bodily tired but a little voice within him feels so depleted, it begins to whisper "Why go on?" However, there is a little spirit in most of us that won't let us stop—won't let us give up the ghost. Something drives him on. However, when a person has suffered so much from nervous illness, that little voice becomes very, very tired and going on to him seems impossible. There may not even seem enough spirit within him to help him to put on his clothes in the morning. His spirit to live on is so fatigued it is as if the vitality within him is sapped almost to its dregs; there seems nothing left within him to draw upon, no bank, no reserve. When, with such utter fatigue, there comes almost no wish to go on, then I call that fatigue, spiritual.

MARIAN: What can you do when someone has reached the point where the voice which says "Why go on?" has become so loud that the person suffering is actually considering suicide? I mean, is that too late to start giving them a reason to live, or hope for peace from suffering?

DOCTOR: Never! because in all of us there is a power which, if we ask for it, will keep us trying. The power is always there if we want it; it's always there; it never, never, never really leaves us. But that person may need outside help.

To begin with, he not only needs the willingness to go on, but he has to be shown clearly how to do it; because those first steps to recovery can be so faltering, so faltering, that he may slip many times.

MARIAN: So how do you go about helping these people who are suffering so badly from any of the fatigues you have been talking about? For example, the nervously ill person who has become a severe agoraphobic?

DOCTOR: Marian, I teach them first to see that they must take all the fight out of their battle. It's a battle all right, but not a battle for fighting. I know people who will think "Well, what do you do in a battle if you don't fight?" But to put it simply, they must first accept the state they're in. I explain nervous fatigue to them, so their bewilderment clears; I explain their symptoms, and this explanation also helps to clear bewilderment. For example, I explain that the erratic banging of their heart is only a temporary upset in the nervous timing of the heartbeat; I explain how adrenalin will accelerate a heart, and how adrenalin is a stress hormone secreted by the adrenal glands when under stress; I explain how in extreme fatigue there is a depletion of the cortisone that our adrenal glands also secrete to combat stress; I explain how fatigue, whether muscular, emotional, mental or spiritual, has a chemical basis. I explain all that, until the sufferer really understands the kind of state he is in. My explanation, his understanding, are the first steps; then he must be prepared to be in the state he is in, to almost relax in it, and to give up the fight, to stop fighting.

MARIAN: That sounds as if he's having to put up with it.

DOCTOR: Quite the opposite. "Putting up with" implies gritting teeth and clenching fists: effort that is going to be more and more exhausting, so that he becomes tenser and tenser. He should accept it with as much relaxation as he can muster. He must float into it; loosen and accept; loosen and accept. An example of this was described well by a woman who hadn't travelled for three or four years and then decided to have a holiday on the Canary Islands. I'm sure I've talked about her before: she was also a good example of floating. She went to the Canary Islands and took my tape recording *Going on Holiday* with her. The first few days were a bit rocky but she said that when she got to Tenerife she even climbed the mountains. She added, "I couldn't believe it", and then she described how, one night at dinner, the panic swept again: "All my feelings!" and she added, "It was roast turkey, my favourite meal. I thought, 'I'll never swallow this!'" and then she said "I heard your voice saying 'Loosen and accept. Loosen and accept.' So I loosened and accepted, and thought then of floating, not fighting. So I ate the soft vegetables: I could swallow the soft vegetables, and by the time the coffee came I was floating fine!"

MARIAN: Are floating and accepting another way of saying "total relaxation"?

DOCTOR: They include total relaxation, but they are relaxation with action—more than just relaxation. The acceptance I teach includes going forward into life, doing what has to be done. That woman did not rush out of the dining room; she stayed at the table and ate her meal. She went forward. Yes, I do mean total relaxation, but with understanding and with a willingness to do what life demands. For instance, if you've got a job to do—suppose you've got to collect your daughter from school—you go and do it. But you do it in a special way; you let your body loosen, you relax towards it, you are prepared to take what comes. That's what I call floating—relax as much as possible and be prepared to take what comes. Even thinking of floating helps. So you float forward into the car and float off and do it. Relaxation is a big part of it, but there is always endeavour, acceptance of whatever comes. You think "I'm going to go forwards by floating; I'm going to do this and I'm going to do it willingly, no struggle, no fight!" Again, if you are so nervously exhausted, so tired in the morning, that you look at your clothes and think "However am I going to put them on?", you should think "I'm not going to struggle with them, I'm going to float into them"—you can even just think "Float, float," and that helps. I had a patient who was an air hostess, taking one of her final exams; she'd had a nervous illness and was very worried because she had to serve a meal to some VIPs. This was part of her examination. She said to me "How am I going to serve them soup with my hands trembling like that?" I said "Float the soup to them, float it, float it!" She came back and said

"I floated the soup. I floated the chicken. I floated everything!" It's a beautiful word, that word "float". I teach it over and over again. When floating on water your body goes this way, that way, with the waves, and it takes it. The sufferer should let his body do the same. If he goes out and is afraid of panicking while out, he should let the panic come—even go towards the panic, not shrink from it. Panic is only an electric flash. Let it pass. As I say so often, even if it seems to singe the roots of your hair. I know that sounds easy to do, and I do know what I'm saying, but it can be done by utter acceptance.

MARIAN: And if you do get an attack of the trembling hands or the knocking knees, when perhaps you're meeting some royal personage, or some very important boss; and when, while you might accept and understand why the knees are knocking and so on—they still knock! Surely there is a point when even floating might not work for you in a situation like that?

DOCTOR: We're talking about two different kinds of people: if you mean the person who is highly strung, and who may easily have trembling hands or knocking knees, or both, when under tension, he or she should be prepared to learn to function with them while they're putting on their little act. However, I'm talking about the nervously ill person, who has the trembling because of his illness but who usually does not have it. He should ask himself what is most important—to be prepared to take the knocking knees and trembling hands, to accept the situation, and still have the courage to see it through? Or—to run away? I ask you, how far can you run away from yourself? How far can you run from trembling hands! You stay, Marian, and you let your knees knock and your hands tremble, but you relax towards that moment, again to the best of your ability. A minister's wife came to me with that very problem: frequently at a meeting she had to serve tea in the best china, and everyone's shaky hand trembles much more when using the best china than with nice solid mugs and solid china. And as she handed out the best china, the cups would surely rattle. I said "Explain to your friends; tell them not to mind your trembling hands; that the tea tastes just as well!" The tension eased—they even joked. After a while her hands trembled no more.

Another girl came to me directly after arriving back from London—she was an Australian—and she'd saved up her little bit of money for a trip to London and she'd had her trip. Unfortunately she had a shock while she was in London and went through a very nervous time, and her hands began to shake. She went from neurologist to psychiatrist, but nothing stopped her shaking hands. She had so little money left that she had to return to Australia: she couldn't get a job with those shaking hands. When she came to me, I said "Let them shake, Helen, let them shake." She answered "Is that all I have to do?" I said "Yes, just let them shake—it's more important that you do your job. Who cares if your hands are shaking? If they shake, say 'I'm sorry my hands shake, but I can still do the job.'" She again said "Is that all I have to do?"; I said "Yes." She said "If only I'd known that in London, I could have stayed!"

I knew a man with the same problem—he said "I can eat in certain restaurants if they give the coffee in a big cup, but in some of these wretched restaurants they give you coffee in those tiny little things, and I'm afraid I'm going to upset the whole caboose!" So I said "Upset it, but see that you upset it into the saucer, not on the tablecloth." He said "You really mean that?" After a few sessions he was no longer tense about the whole program and could drink coffee in restaurants.

MARIAN: It's very interesting, but earlier you made the comment, "Relaxation with action," and by that you didn't mean "lying on the bed." Now there must be times, though, when perhaps, particularly with older people, they do need to lie down, when they do need to replenish their store of energy. How do you decide between a patient who needs rest and the patient who really should not be lying there brooding in bed?

DOCTOR: I teach them how to decide for themselves. Your question is interesting, Marian, because one woman wrote to me and said that she had been so pleased with the progress she'd made that she hoped to tell her doctor how wonderful she felt and that it had all been due to my book, but she added "In your book you said 'Keep off that bed in the daytime!' Well, I kept off the bed in the daytime, all day, but now I'm really so tired and exhausted that I have to go back to the doctor to tell him that I'm more run-down than before I read your book." So you see, doctors have to be so careful about what they say. She'd had an operation, and needed that rest, but the poor old soul had kept going because Dr Weekes had happened to say so. I was upset by that. I didn't know about the operation!

MARIAN: Surely some people when they're very depressed just want to pull a pillow over their head and not face the day, and then stay like that for a long time?

DOCTOR: Everything depends on their attitude. Many will ask me how much they should do or how much they shouldn't do—it depends entirely on how they look at it. For example, if they do too much one day and are tired the next day, as long as they think "So, what the heck, I did a bit too much yesterday, but what does that matter?" or if they think that they didn't do enough yesterday; none of it matters as long as they're not upset by whatever they did or didn't do. If they see that each is a different day, and that each carries them forward, if they can think "I have my program, I have my understanding, my body will heal itself if I stand out of its way and let it."Attitude, attitude, attitude.

MARIAN: Another of the concepts that's important to you is that people have to let "time pass"—is that because you feel that time, in the end, is the healer?

DOCTOR: Time is a healer; however it heals most quickly if the sufferer is on the right track. When nerves become sensitised, although they're not physically injured nerves (as in the sense that a cut nerve is), they are still altered nerves. We call them "aroused". They are chemically altered and have to heal in just the same way as they would if they had been physically injured. This takes time. So the person who can come to a doctor and get thorough, satisfactory understanding and leave feeling happy, must yet know that they will still have to face, accept, float and let time pass. I explain that there is no switch that will desensitise their nerves overnight. Patients, when they leave happy, still have to be prepared to wake in the morning perhaps feeling early foreboding, even a quickly beating heart, and other nervous symptoms; they may still feel trembling, weakness, tingling and—above all—foreboding; their nerves are still sensitised. This is why I stress that they must not be impatient with time. I teach them to see themselves as an animal, driven forward with a long stick and a carrot at the end of the stick. They must think to themselves, "All right, I'll push the carrot a bit further away, just a bit further forward, and I'm not going to get upset because today I'm not feeling so wonderful. Time will eventually heal my sensitisation." With that attitude, letting time pass is certainly the healer, even though setbacks are almost inevitable. Doctors should prepare their patients for this. They should be taught all about setbacks, even to welcome them.

MARIAN: To welcome them?

DOCTOR: Yes, because it's during a setback that sufferers learn what they must do to get out of it. They must not expect to walk out of the doctor's office cured— although some have done that. I like my patients to have setbacks because they always say they learn more in a setback. I teach them that while they may think "Here it is again!", they should also think "Here's another chance to practise what I've been taught", and to remember that with each setback they have another chance to build my teaching into themselves; another chance to help build the little voice that will say "It's all right, old chap, you've been here before, you know the way out. You know it!" It's that little voice that catches them when they fall—that is their cushion. Time helps build that voice and that's why time is so important. Time is the healer, but the sufferer must understand what he's doing and must not just leave his recovery to chance. He must be taught to heal himself. I do encourage all my patients to heal themselves; to do it on their own feet, not to make me their healer. I never let them depend on me, only on what I teach.

MARIAN: So do you ever help them with any form of tranquilliser, or anything like that? Or are you saying that they do much of this without tranquillisers?

DOCTOR: I've used so few tranquillisers in my treatment, so few. But some do need them, while others can manage just with explanation; perhaps very constant explanation;

but they are able to accept the symptoms, whatever the symptoms are.

MARIAN: So, when would you use a tranquilliser?

DOCTOR: I use a tranquilliser when the sufferer is so exhausted, and painfully sensitised when he comes to me. Usually, in the past when I was in practice, many of my patients would have already seen psychiatrists (I am a physician, of course), and heard so many different opinions, that when they came to me they were pretty well exhausted, I can tell you. However, for me to prescribe tranquillisers for a few days often gave them some rest, some peace for a little while. If the sensitisation was extremely severe I would continue the tranquillisation perhaps for a few weeks, but I would always supervise it; and when I stopped it I would stop very gradually. I don't believe in stopping tranquillisation suddenly, I don't believe in this "cold turkey" business at all. Today a lot is written about tranquillisers, unfortunately by people who've had no experience whatever in using them. I was talking the other day to the superintendent of one of our psychiatric hospitals in London and he said that it was a pity so much adverse criticism had been written lately in the media about tranquillisers, because for some people they really were life-saving.

Used intelligently, yes. But here again the difference in age must be considered. An older person may need mild tranquillisation, where a younger person can do without. I should say that if I had an elderly patient, I'm much more likely to help them with a tranquilliser, or much less likely to take them off tranquillisers, than I am a younger person. While I like to get young people off tranquillisation as soon as possible, I'm not anxious to get a woman in her late seventies or eighties off tranquillisers. As we get older, it's almost as if our nervous system more easily gets sensitised. You must surely have met grandma who, although she loves the boys, can stand them only for a short while when they come to visit her? She soon retreats into her bedroom—poor old grandma! Now if grandma had a mild tranquilliser when the boys arrived, she might even enjoy the visit.

I think tranquillisers have their part to play, especially, as I have said, for old people. After all, as we get old we may lose some teeth—sometimes all of them—much of our hearing, and sight; we might also lose some of our ability to take things calmly.

MARIAN: What about going into hospital? I know of cases where doctors have tried to help nervously ill people and have in the end said "You'll have to come into hospital!" In hospital they've either had drug treatment or been encouraged to go out in the care of a nurse, to gradually win confidence about going back into cars and buses, and that type of thing. In your opinion, is that a useful thing to do—to actually go into hospital and get away from the house, the pressures, the family?

DOCTOR: For a housewife, yes, sometimes; yes, it can be a help. Sometimes the actual pressures of having to look after a house at the same time as perhaps not sleeping, or being heavy with drugs that have been prescribed by her doctor, become a stress that really holds a patient back. Mind you, if she has the kind of doctor who will help her along with explanations and support, and give her a program and show her how to use it, she can do it all without going into hospital; so much depends on the circumstances. For some it can be a great help if the sufferer can find peace in hospital. For example, if it's a good hospital, with skilled nurses to take her out and understand her illness, and who can also show her what to do. It has to be a nurse who understands that she must not boss the patient, or treat her like a child; on the other hand, she must not shelter her too much.

MARIAN: But if you know that there isn't that sort of guidance in hospital, is it better to stay out of hospital?

DOCTOR: You know, you're giving me a difficult question, because . . .

MARIAN: It's just that I thought you weren't terribly keen on people going into hospital. What is your opinion of electric shock treatment?

DOCTOR: For severely depressed people whom one can no longer contact satisfactorily by talking to them, then it can save them much suffering. Here again, it must be used judiciously. I never advise it for a person in an anxiety state. I've never yet seen it cure a person in an anxiety state, but I have seen a severely depressed person come back happily to normality, so that they have been able to carry on. And if they are normally optimistic, they will usually make a good recovery. I remember one little Italian mother who was so upset by her husband's death (I think I put her in one of my books) that I couldn't get across to her by talking, she was so depressed. She had only four or five shock treatments and when she came back to see me she was almost bubbling with optimism. She said she must return as quickly as possible to the farm, to help harvest the grapes, because they'd be getting too ripe and the men picking them had to be fed. That was all she was thinking about. She didn't mention her husband again to me. She never looked back. So here again, with shock treatment, you have to judge it according to the patient. You can't condemn it unthinkingly.

MARIAN: Are there times when you have to treat not just the patient, but support and help the family too? Surely sometimes the family either can't cope with the patient's problems or doesn't understand them; is that a major treatment—getting the family to understand what you're trying to do for the patient?

DOCTOR: Yes, one of the major difficulties is getting the family to understand. I remember one Italian husband to whom I was trying to explain what to do: I met him in the garden and I thought he was listening to me very attentively, but when I'd finished he just looked at me vaguely and said, "But why not the chippa-potata? Why is it always the masha-potata? I want chippa-potata! She's not the woman I married!" She cooked him "chippa-potata" that night.

MARIAN (*Interrupting*): Sorry, I'm just stopping you because you're rubbing your blouse and we're picking it up on the mike.

DOCTOR: Sorry! Anyhow, eventually I got him around. My way of approaching the husband—and it's usually the husband, unfortunately, not always, but usually—is to appeal to him by telling him that I consider he is the wise member of the family who could help me. I usually say that I am asking him because he understands these things. Of course, he doesn't understand a bit, but once I say I think he is, he looks wise and when I ask him to help he very often does. You never get anywhere by upbraiding him and telling him how difficult he is. But you get a lot of help from the family if you get them on your side. It can be so important to get them on your side.

MARIAN: Because it must be a particularly difficult time for them, if the person—the mother or perhaps the father—is the one who is suffering from obsessive behaviour?

DOCTOR: Very hard, Marian.

MARIAN: You've talked about agoraphobia and the anxiety

state. But what can you actually do if someone has developed a number of obsessions? Obsessions multiply over a period of years for some people. I know you have a special technique, haven't you, that you try to teach them?

DOCTOR: Indeed. I call it "glimpsing". And it works. You remember the patient in the last BBC talk we had? [Chapter Two] She was ill for nine years with many obsessions and she'd had, as she said, every treatment in the book. I had a Christmas card from her this year, saying "Thank you for the peace in my head." That was beautiful. That card is on my dressing table.

You can teach a person with obsessions that these have arisen because of mental and emotional fatigue. An obsession is a repeated thought in a very tired mind. First I teach them the truth, the reality behind the obsession. For instance, one woman would clear out her refrigerator many times each day. Imagine having to wash your refrigerator and having to take everything out half a dozen times a day! I was able to explain to her that there were no germs there that could hurt her through contamination in that refrigerator, because it kept everything so cold. I even took swabbings throughout her house and had them cultured. Every culture came back negative. So I taught her to sit beside me and to "glimpse". To glimpse, even if only for a brief moment, that there were no germs there. No pathological germs that could harm her. You see, that was the truth, the reality. If she could glimpse that truth, for a moment only, during that moment she was seeing the truth. Of course I knew that a moment later she'd be back in the obsession, especially when she left me. Those frightening thoughts had come so frequently, that they automatically went "Whoosh" down those old, well-worn tracks in her mind, almost automatically. But I warned her of that too. I said "Just as you would practise the piano daily, sit and practise glimpsing. While you talk to me you understand that there are no germs to hurt you. When you are away from me, the obsession returns; that's when you must practise holding that glimpse, if only for a fleeting moment. Gradually, very very gradually, that moment will be established, as the right way of looking at the problem. Finally, what was an obsession will become only a strange thought and as such can be laughed at and dismissed."

You remember the woman that we showed on the BBC two years ago who was a severe case (the doctors at the hospital she attended were even talking about a leucotomy for her)? You know, Marian, I saw that woman only once. We had only telephone and tape recordings to use, and the telephone was between England and Australia, which was very expensive, and yet she is cured. She's the one who sent the card at Christmas time saying "Thanks for the peace in my head." Glimpsing, glimpsing, glimpsing!

But these people need a doctor who knows something about glimpsing and who is interested enough to find the right point of view behind the obsession, and who will help them to glimpse it until it becomes reality. Therapists give a lot of drugs for obsession. But the answer is rarely in drugs.

MARIAN: And people who have suffered nervous illness for many, many years—apart from getting very depressed about it—must also be left with a very low sense of self-esteem?

DOCTOR: Oh, yes.

MARIAN: You know, I remember reading in your book that someone once said to you "Is it just that I'm a weak character, Doctor?"

DOCTOR: When a sufferer's emotions are much exaggerated with fatigue they often respond to every changing thought. As I have said in one of my earlier books, it is as if a little child could lead them. And this is what makes them feel that they are a weak character, Marian. They are so vulnerable to suggestion that they feel disintegrated; the quick, almost flashing, connection between thought and feeling brings bewildering complications. The rapid emotional reaction to a thought is so important, it is then that the sufferer feels as though a little child could lead him. When like that, he must lose confidence in himself; it's inevitable. The nervously ill person begins to get confidence back only when he's taken his first faltering steps towards recovery, *while depending on his own initiative*. Finally there are times when he gets such a feeling of confidence he thinks "This is me at last! This is me at last!" That feeling may last only a fleeting second and be gone. He should let it go! Let it go! Let it go *willingly*! Once he's glimpsed that feeling of integration, when it goes I can assure him it will always return until it is finally the established mood. Then, not only will he have the confidence he used to have, he will have the added confidence of having brought himself up out of despair. One patient said in an interview on television, when I asked if she were happy, "Oh yes, I'm happy—you don't know heaven until you've known hell." And that is the truth; you only know confidence when you know what it is to be without it. We're not born confident. Many people whom we think are confident are only self-assertive. It's when you have no confidence, and then have built it step by step that it will not leave you.

MARIAN: In fact, they're building up a sense of courage, aren't they, over a period of years? But through this long struggle, you do see a lot of these people as being very courageous?

DOCTOR: Yes, these are some of the bravest people I have known. They tackle things when they have almost nothing within themselves with which to tackle them. But, of course, that is the best time to try. I think those who have the opportunity to test themselves in the fire like this are so lucky. They learn what inner strength is. They know what life is all about; they know what "to struggle" means and then they learn by contrast, they discover what beauty is all about. And they know what true peace is. In fact—they just "know"!

MARIAN: Helping people like this must take up a lot of your nervous energy? Has it been a battle for you, doing so much work for people who needed to draw such a lot on your strength? Have you found that it's been tiring work over the years?

DOCTOR: No, Marian. When you do something you enjoy, it doesn't really tire you. At the end of a busy day's work, I'd hear the telephone in the dining room ringing as I got out of my car; I'd probably answer it before I had dinner, but that still didn't take a lot out of me. Well, I'm 80 now, so it hasn't taken everything, has it?

MARIAN: In fact, the work won't let you go, because you're still writing books—you've just written your fourth book on nervously ill people, called *More Help for Your Nerves*.

DOCTOR: Yes, that's right.

MARIAN: Do you find other doctors are listening to you now? Your patients listen, I know, and I know you've lectured a lot in the United Kingdom and America. You don't seem to find very much time to relax, I notice! But do you feel that the professionals are actually listening to what you're saying now?

DOCTOR: Yes, they are. Many letters come, saying "My doctor told me to read your book!" and the doctors write, asking for the tape recordings. The tapes are being widely used now in psychiatric hospitals—especially in the United Kingdom and in America. Very, very much so. It's taken 20 years, Marian. In America I was guest speaker at the annual conference of the Phobia Society of America. The audience was practically all made up of psychiatrists and psychotherapists. In the end truth will come out, even if it takes a long time; it must come in the end. It spreads because it produces results. I probably won't be here to see it firmly established, but I know that it will be. There are many clinics now throughout America and Canada using my work; so many and here in England also. So many small groups are starting up and they write and ask me to help them. A woman recently wrote, I think I showed you her picture, and that was lovely.

MARIAN: You can tell everybody about that photograph, Doctor.

DOCTOR: Well, this was an agoraphobic woman who'd been so agoraphobic that she hadn't been away from her home for years, and she sent me a photograph of herself down at Brighton, and she wrote "Look at this—it's what your work has done for us!" This was the first time she'd been to the seaside for years, and she held in her arms a little boy of seven, who was looking down at the water. He'd never seen water like that before, and she was holding him there, and he was splashing his legs, just feeling the water, while she looked down at him, ecstatically. This came last week. Yes, the work is everywhere; work like that must spread.

MARIAN: It must give you a very good feeling to know this?

DOCTOR: Of course. When you get old, Marian, it doesn't

seem to matter how happy you've been, all that really matters is what you've done. Having done something to help other people is a wonderful cushion of support with which to face old age. I haven't worked alone, you know. I've been helped so much by others, who for years have stood by my side, especially here in England. There have been three people in particular who've done much of the hack work for me; they've gone out and carried heavy loads of cassettes and books to the post office day after day and they've done that in all weathers, for nearly 20 years. That's a long time. I'm very happy to have this opportunity to mention them, because I thank them so dearly. One of them was the woman who came to clean for us. I used to call her "Mrs Newt". I thank you now, Mrs Newt. And incidentally, many, many people thank you also.

MARIAN: Thank you, Dr Weekes, thank you very much.

DOCTOR: Thank you, Marian, for giving me the chance to talk like this.

5

Talk Given at White Plains Hospital, New York, 1983

I explained earlier, in Chapter One, how my teaching differed from the orthodox psychiatric treatment of my time; I also explained how today (1989) it has become accepted and practised worldwide by doctors and other therapists. To achieve this I had to live and crusade through 25 years, when, for most of the time, I stood alone beside the teaching. Many times I have comforted nervously ill people who complained of not being understood by their family and friends, by explaining that nervous illness can be a very lonely business. I also assure them here that trying to establish an unorthodox view of treatment for nervous illness can also be a very lonely business. I felt, for years, rather like a female Don Quixote, crossing lances even with members of my own profession! Although I never doubted, I was lonely.

So it was with much joy that I found my work becoming known and appreciated by doctors at the White Plains Hospital, New York.

This was primarily because of Dr Manuel Zane, the Director of the Phobia Clinic and Attending Psychiatrist at that hospital. I had met Dr Zane in the mid-1970s and then later in 1977 at a psychiatric conference in New York. From then on we have been friends, appreciating and sympathising with each other's work. So, giving this talk at the White Plains Hospital on my way home to Australia in 1983 was not unexpected.

My work was also acclaimed by Dr Robert DuPont, Professor of Clinical Psychiatry at Georgetown University, Washington DC. I first met Dr DuPont when he was President of the Phobia Society of America, a society dedicated to the establishment of modern understanding and treatment of the anxiety state and phobias. From its foundation in 1983, this society has grown perceptibly, and now supports clinical branches throughout the United States.

To each of these psychiatrists, Dr Manuel Zane and Dr Robert DuPont, I am deeply indebted.

DR ZANE: I'm Dr Zane, Director of the Phobia Clinic here at the hospital . . . and it's an unusual pleasure for me to see Dr Weekes again. She reminds me that we were together at a meeting in 1977. The thing that I remember was the depth of her observations and the lack of appreciation, it seemed to me, by most of the audience of what she had to say. I was at least able to comment publicly that Dr Weekes has been a real pioneer in this field and the thing that's remarkable about her is that people have come to me over the years, talking about her. I first learned about her from a patient of mine. I was already doing this kind of work on my own, having come out of internal medicine in the field of physical rehabilitation, and working with people who were physically handicapped—but when this patient told me about Dr Weekes's book (I think it was *Hope and Help for Your Nerves*) I went and read it and I was amazed by the humanness of the approach, the observations that were made by her of people, and I really almost couldn't understand this because being myself a psychiatrist, psychoanalytically trained, *I knew that this was something different: she was coming to us from where the patient is, and not from on top, where we are telling the patient what it's all about—why you're the way you are—but she was listening to what people say, and it's clear to me that this was an outstanding aspect of her presentation, that she understood*, and then people would be coming to me over the years and telling me they had read Claire Weekes's book and I'd say "Well, what do you think of it?" and they'd say "I never believed there was anybody who could understand me that way—that was I" and I agree with that. I think we were most fortunate to have Claire Weekes make this long journey from Australia, and to come to us and to be willing to just sit with us and chat with us. Without any further ado, I want to take this occasion to welcome Dr Weekes and have her share with us whatever she is inclined to talk about.

DR WEEKES: Thank you, Dr Zane. When I was first asked to come here, I understood that I was to talk to a small group of people, I thought about 12 or 13, and answer questions. So I said—in ignorance and innocence—"Of course I will." The first thing that my friend in Bronxville, with whom I'm staying, showed me when I arrived on the scene was a notice from a newspaper, "Dr Weekes will make a speech and then answer questions." Heavens! I thought, I haven't got any speech ready to make! You see, I'm the sort of person who, when I have to make a speech, likes to prepare something. Do you remember there was a story about Billy Graham, how in one of his early speeches, when he'd worked so hard and he knew it so well, and when there were so many important people there, when he got up to make his speech, he was through it in five minutes—he went "Whirrrrr" to the end; that's very easily done, and I didn't want to do it, so I thought "What the heck am I going to do? A speech? Two days to get over jetlag and a speech?" So I quickly thought of something: I'm going to have sitting here with me, an imaginary patient, one that I have interviewed hundreds of times: her name is Jess (she wants a name, so she's called Jess) and she's sitting here in this chair [*Dr Weekes points to the empty chair beside her*], and you'll have to see the back of Jess's head, but that'll be all right [*Laughter*].

Now Jess didn't want to come and see me because she wasn't convinced there was a doctor who could help her—you see, Jess had already seen so many doctors. [*Dr Weekes addresses the chair*] That's right, isn't it, Jess? And then her husband picked up a book from the library, and, as he read, he thought "This is Jess!", so he took it home and read some of it to Jess. Jess actually read the book, she read it and she read it and she hadn't been able to read before, and when she finished it, she said "I'd like to see that doctor!" So her husband brought her, didn't he, Jess? And she sat in my surgery, and while she sat before me she almost tore her handkerchief into shreds, she was so frightened. I said to her, quietly, "Now, Jess, if I had a magic wand, what would you like me to wave away?" and Jess said "Stop me being frightened, Doctor, I'm frightened of everything, I'm frightened all the time, Doctor. I have a husband and I have two children, but I have to do all the housework and I can't do it, Doctor, I can't do any of it. The doctors say there's nothing wrong with me, but I know I'm sick, Doctor. I'm so tired, and I can't seem to get my breath properly and when I wake up in the morning I can't move, I'm that tired, and I get so depressed, and there's a sort of tight band around my head, and it's there all day and Aspros won't move it. And then Johnny, the little one—he's two—he's only got to cry or shout at me and my stomach goes into a sort of clutch, and if I get up quickly to go to Mary—Mary's five—or run to see where she is, my legs just go to jelly, they have no strength, they wobble and sometimes I even fall over. And in the morning when I have to do the washing-up, I feel so faint. Will I faint, Doctor? I feel I'm going to faint at the sink—will I really faint?

DOCTOR TO IMAGINARY PATIENT: Jess, how long have you been like this?

IMAGINARY PATIENT [*Doctor imitates Jess*]: Ever since the last baby was born, Doctor. That's about two years.

DOCTOR: Did you have to come home from the hospital and start in on this work straight away? Too soon?

IMAGINARY PATIENT: Yes, there was nobody to help me, Doctor.

DOCTOR: Your mother couldn't have helped you?

IMAGINARY PATIENT: My mother was sick, having a hysterectomy, Doctor.

DOCTOR: No sister?

IMAGINARY PATIENT: Only me. But my husband, he'd get up at night to the baby sometimes, but the baby cried a lot; and a lot of night feeding, and I think that's when it started, when I thought "How will I ever cope with them all while I feel like this?"

DOCTOR: Jess, have you any help in the home now?

IMAGINARY PATIENT: No, Doctor.

DOCTOR: Couldn't you possibly have a fortnight's break?

IMAGINARY PATIENT: Where would I go, Doctor?

DOCTOR TO AUDIENCE: So this is the history of Jess. It goes on and on, you see.

IMAGINARY PATIENT: But Doctor, I usedn't to be like this—I could do everything: I could wash and iron and look after the house and the two children, and I could not only take the little one to school but I could bring Elizabeth back from school (Elizabeth is my friend's little girl). But now Elizabeth's mother picks Mary up every day and she takes her to school and she brings her back with Elizabeth. And I don't see how I can ever get over this, Doctor.

DOCTOR: Is that the lot? Have you told me everything? Everything that worries you?

IMAGINARY PATIENT: Well, there are these funny thoughts.

DOCTOR: What funny thoughts do you get, Jess?

IMAGINARY PATIENT: If I go to the ball game and I'm there with all the people, I think terrible thoughts, Doctor—I can't even tell you.

DOCTOR: Yes you can, they're not so funny to me, you know.

IMAGINARY PATIENT: Well, if I see a nun in the street I think terrible things about her.

[*Interruption while microphone is changed, as people at the back could not hear*]

DOCTOR: [*Reintroduces Jess to the audience*] Jess said that she gets the quickly beating heart, whatever she does; she'll find it banging against the sink as she washes up. As she goes to bed, maybe just as she's going off to sleep, it will palpitate and she'll feel as if her head is swinging on the pillow, just like a pendulum and then she said she gets so screwed up with any little extra worry and she gets this feeling of "horse's hoof" in her stomach, and she feels she must, must get ease from that. And the only thing that will give her ease, she finds, is a Valium or a Serepax, or perhaps a talk with a kind friend, but also then time has to pass before the ease comes and I said to her "Well, Jess, what else worries you? And you told me, Jess, didn't you?" Yes, she said she gets very, very weak, very tired. When she wakes up in the morning she can hardly get out of bed to point her body at the work [*Doctor turns to Jess*] and Jess, although your husband is very understanding, he still can't understand why you get so very tired, can he?

IMAGINARY PATIENT: No, Doctor, he can't, that's right, that's right. No, he simply can't understand, Doctor.

DOCTOR TURNS TO THE AUDIENCE: No, he can't see much work done, and the beds aren't properly made and the dinner's not that hot either, so he thinks "What *is* she doing all day to be so tired?" and she feels so guilty about it, because she thinks, too, that she hasn't been doing that much. But I explained to her that all these symptoms: the terrible tension headache, the clutching hand on the tummy, the weakness, the tremor, the muscle jerks, the anxiety, the quickly beating heart, the sweating, the waking up as though something terrible is about to happen—[*Doctor Weekes turns towards the empty chair and addresses Jess*] You get that, do you, Jess, waking up as if something is about to happen? You told me about that, didn't you? And how you had to keep telling yourself all the time that nothing terrible was going to happen?

IMAGINARY PATIENT: Yes, that's right, Doctor.

DOCTOR: I've seen many Jesses before, you know—many times. So all these symptoms, as I have explained to Jess, are the symptoms of stress, and they come about in a very special way. You see, we can take a lot of stress, provided our organs are well supplied with the chemicals that they need to make the necessary hormones to combat stress. That's fine at first, but the supply of chemicals runs down when stress is constant. How vulnerable the sufferer becomes then, to every passing fear!

A person like Jess, when she comes home from hospital with one little baby tucked under her arm, and another pulling at her dress, can feel so weak (they probably did take a haemoglobin at the hospital and it was possibly a bit low), and yet she may have had to get up at night to feed the baby, and not get enough sleep, and get her husband off to work while she was like that . . .

And now I've forgotten where I was—I'm 80 years of age [*Audience applauds*]—I wanted to get that clap because I think a person who gets to be 80 has done jolly well! [*More applause*] . . . Anyhow, the chemicals in Jess's body that were coping with her stress were getting depleted. Her body was demanding more and more chemicals, more and more, but her exhaustion was such because the supply of chemicals was getting exhausted, so she was really depleted. I explained this to her—that this was the bogeyman sitting on her shoulder; she wasn't going mental, she wasn't even strange—she was just an ordinary person whose physical demands to cope with stress weren't being met. Not being met; and you know Jess didn't eat enough. [*Doctor turns towards Jess*] You wouldn't sit with the family, or if you did, all eyes were on your plate, to see that you finished, and you couldn't stand that, so you'd creep away with the plate and eat a little bit and throw the rest in the trashcan. Because our stomach, of all organs, weeps when any other organ in the body is having trouble; it weeps in sympathy, so we don't want to eat. And this is the time when, most of all, we need food, to supply the chemicals that we need to replenish our adrenal glands, and other glands, to combat the stress. And, Jess, you'd just break an egg in a glass and beat it around and drink it—that'd be your day's food, wouldn't it, Jess? No extra vitamins! I had to teach you, didn't I, about taking more food and giving yourself enough vitamins, and you were a good girl, Jess, you really were.

So, I explained the pattern of stress to Jess, and explained how, when she felt fear, and she felt it so often, the fear would alert her nervous system, "arouse" her nerves, and I explained that when nerves are aroused they become altered and respond much more intensely, and much more rapidly. For example, if there's a little girl waiting at the window, in the evening, for her father to come home, who's usually had too much to drink and gets argumentative and beats Mum up in the hall, then that little girl will run and hide under the bed as soon as he comes in. Even before he comes in you'll find her listening at the window for his footsteps, and when she hears him talking to the neighbours, her heart will begin to race, and she'll dive for the bed. And sometimes when she listens at the window she won't even have to wait to hear him talk to the neighbours, her nerves are so aroused she'll even hear the bus door slam. She has become sensitised to the sound of her father's homecoming. You can put it scientifically by saying "reverberated circuits in our nervous system bring a heightened response." If nerves could not be sensitised, aroused, if we all remained calm, no matter what happened, no matter what stress we had, I doubt if there would be any anxiety states. But our body isn't built like that: nerves do get aroused, reverberated circuits do bring a heightened response. Instead of repeated impulses being blocked off, they are allowed to go through, again and again, so that a slightly anxious feeling grows into a pang of panic, and the panic itself becomes augmented, augmented, augmented, until Jess got a great "Whoosh" of panic, which seemed to burn the very roots of her hair, and by that time she'd really got something to contend with. A cold blast of wind alone may bring panic when a patient is aroused to it. A sad sight will seem tragic: she'll cry at the movies when normally she wouldn't cry. Even a little joy may be felt almost hysterically. It's very hard to cope with yourself when you're like that—you do think you're going nuts, and yet it's no more than being highly sensitised. And extreme sensitisation so depletes adrenal glands that they bring utter, utter tiredness. It's a tiredness that seems beyond a tiredness; it's a tiredness that seems not only of the body but also of the spirit; because many of these people feel they no longer have, not so much the wish to survive, but the will to do it. Surviving from one day to the next asks for more strength than these people think they have.

These are bewildered people. They have courage, hope, desire to get better, love for their children so they will try to get better for them; yes, but a big slice of their bewilderment is ignorance, and they hope that some day they'll find a doctor who will explain to them what it's all about, tell them what to do, instead of just handing them tranquillisers or antidepressants.

Well, I told all that to Jess, and then I followed by doing what I did at the end of most of my sessions with my patients. I would say to her "Now, Jess, before you go home, put into your own words what I want you to do." I wanted to know, before Jess left, that she really understood what I wanted her to do. If she understood she would say "You want me to accept all the strange feelings, Doctor, and yet to go on, do what I have to do with them there."

DOCTOR TO IMAGINARY PATIENT: Yes, I want you to really

accept them, Jess, willingly, too. Don't think Dr Weekes says "I've got to put up with this" and "I've got to put up with that"; don't clench your teeth, that tension is going to squeeze out more stress hormone, and your adrenal glands will be more depleted. Relax, Jess, just flop in your chair like that [*Dr Weekes shows how to "flop"*] and say "Whatever my body does to me, I accept it as willingly as I can."

IMAGINARY PATIENT: Even the panic flash, Doctor?

DOCTOR: Even the panic flash. But of course while she's so tired, so worn out, I've found that even a couple of days' sleep, with somebody else watching the babies, is a tremendous help. It gives Jess fresh courage and fresh hope. And before she goes home, I say to her "Jess, where will you be tomorrow at half past eleven?"

IMAGINARY PATIENT: I'll be home, Doctor.

DOCTOR TO AUDIENCE: And then I give a little ring on my bell and my secretary, Jean, comes in and I say "Jean, tomorrow morning at half past eleven, will you remind me to ring Mrs Macarthur?" And Jess looks up at me and says "Will you really ring me tomorrow, Doctor, at half past eleven?"

DOCTOR TO IMAGINARY PATIENT: I won't forget, Jess.

DOCTOR TO AUDIENCE: And I don't forget, and I ring her every day until I see her the following week. Then it's not so much hard work for me, when she comes the next time, the following Tuesday. By the time I see her the following week, I've got her walking down the street, walking to the pillarbox, doing things like that.

Oh, and before I let most patients with agoraphobia leave me, I make them go downstairs, down the stairs— I never insist on the lift—to buy jelly beans at the chemist on the first floor. And the chemist used to have his counter packed with bags of jelly beans. He said to me one day

"Doctor, that's a funny medicine you use! All your patients come for jelly beans!" People who had thought they couldn't walk before they came to me, when they left me were able to go down four storeys and buy jelly beans and come back.

I had an American once who rang me, and he was attached to the Consulate, and I always left some of my books in my office for people who were going to see me, to read before they did see me. So, they'd pick up a book, take it away, and when they returned I knew I didn't have to go over a lot of ground—they'd already read it. And he came and got the books on a Friday, and rang me on the Monday and said his appointment was on Tuesday. And then he said "Dr Weekes, I read your book and I don't need to keep that appointment— I'm cured!" so I said, "Well, that's fantastic, I'll cancel the appointment." "Oh no, no. My wife, she's going to pieces—she needs the appointment." [*Laughter*]

Well, I wasn't going to make a speech tonight, so I haven't made a speech: anyhow, I didn't have a speech ready to make. But I hope you learnt something from Jess, and now you can ask me anything you like, any question you like, which I'll answer if I know the answer.

QUESTIONS FROM THE AUDIENCE

QUESTIONER: Dr Weekes, you were starting to tell us about Jess's queer feelings, and then you were interrupted.

DOCTOR: Was I? Yes, that's right. Well, they were frightening feelings. You see, when people have been thinking of themselves all day, and a nervously ill person does that, their thoughts may become very peculiar. In fact, they try them out to see how peculiar they can be. They'll think "Am I really mad? Can I really think like that? How much worse could it be? What else could I think?" And things look grotesque to them, perhaps a little shade on a nun's lip will look like a black moustache and they'll think "She's a man in nun's clothing!" Little things will turn and twist and look awful, and they'll think "Well, now I really am going mad!" Don't trust those thoughts when you're nervously ill. If you have them, let them come; remember that just as you cry too much at a sad movie when you're sensitised, so you see the grotesque much too grotesquely also. *They are only thoughts*, but fear of them can hinder your getting better.

While I'm talking about strange, grotesque thoughts, I want to talk about other strange experiences that come particularly during recovery—just when you think you are better, the quietness within yourself, the sudden strangeness of feeling better, can seem hard to bear. One woman said "I'm more at home in my illness! This quietness, this waiting for something to happen, is too strange!" She reminded me of a little Irish girl I met in a train in Ireland. The sun came out suddenly and, as we'd had rain for weeks and weeks, I moved along my seat to get into the sun. But the girl opposite moved out of it. She looked at me apologetically and explained "I don't like the sun! I'm not used to it!" So, when you are recovering and you are especially aware suddenly of the uncanny, quiet sensation of feeling better, don't shrink from it; think, instead, "I'm not going to be like that Irish girl! I'm not going to move away!" and don't try to move away, stay in the moment of strange quiet. Let the quietness be your bit of sunshine! Don't be afraid of it!

I always say the time spent recovering can be so

strange. Sometimes you may be tempted to think "I don't want to recover if I have to face all the responsibilities that will come. I'll never be able to do it!" People who feel this way imagine themselves having to face recovery while they are as they are at that time—still ill, still sensitised, still ill. But recovery doesn't work like that. There are very few sudden recoveries (although they can occur); time usually takes you very gently. You may have many strange experiences to go through, as I've just been trying to tell you. Take each one unquestioningly, knowing that each day you get a firmer foundation, it grows under your very feet, you build on that; you build on a foundation that time gradually presents you after all the strange experiences; in fact, because of those experiences.

Now the biggest foundation of all is setback itself: never, never be sorry when you have a setback; it's the best building stone of all, because when you go through setback, each one gives you an opportunity to practise once more what you must do to get well. It's only when you have learnt how to come through setback on your own efforts, that finally it doesn't matter whether it comes or not, that's when you're really recovering.

Now, don't be disturbed by anything I tell you, because I'm also going to show you how to cope with such situations. Here's one situation: long after you think you've recovered, when you're quite well, stress can still bring back symptoms that remind you of your previous nervous illness, and you may be really shocked by the sudden appearance of these old symptoms. You thought you'd never have them again. But there they are. Don't panic and try to run away from them, don't lose your head! So many do, you know, I've met them in full flight! And I've had to say to them "Halt, halt, stop running!" Examine the situation, look, you're only getting stress symptoms back. They're very much the same symptoms as you get if suddenly you had fantastically good news! If you heard your daughter at school had all As, your legs could go weak and wobbly and your heart could race—they're the same symptoms, except that they have a different meaning! Stop and have a good look at the sudden arrival of symptoms. Analyse what's happened to you, recognise that it's the same old stress, don't let it panic you, don't let it bluff you. "Halt" is the word: halt, and take a good look. Dr Zane teaches you this when he teaches you "contextual therapy". This is what he means: don't let it bluff you into blindly running away. Take the blinkers off your eyes, and examine it well. Dissect it, analyse it, and see it for what it is—pure bluff, and if the symptoms stay for a while longer, accept the fact that you have resensitised yourself, that you may still be sensitised tomorrow and the next day. It doesn't matter how long the sensitisation lasts, accept it all until finally it dies down, the symptoms of stress no longer matter. That is the big key—no longer mattering is the key, not a sudden disappearance. In the middle of having them all, you can suddenly get the feeling "I know them, I know them well, I've been through them, they really don't matter!"; that's when the light suddenly shines and the pathway to recovery lies illuminated before you, that's the light that is so wonderful to feel.

Before you ask any more questions, I'd like to tell you about a clinic in Toronto. The director wrote to me and said "Dr Weekes, do you mind if we put some of your sayings on to biros which we hand out to patients?", and I thought "What a good idea." And they sent me one of these biros and on it they had printed

"Recovery lies in the places and experiences you fear."
And that's just where it lies—not in your ability to avoid
the places or experiences, not in your ability to go so
far without panicking, and run back home before you
panic again, and then later, or the next day, go a little
bit further, and the next day see if you can go even
further without panicking. If you try to get better like
that you'll be caught for sure, horribly caught. Recovery
truly lies in the experiences and the places you fear.
That is where you will gradually learn to take whatever
happens and to make it no longer matter. You can do
it all, you can do anything, with your hands sweating,
with your hands trembling, the panic racing—there's
nothing you can't do if you are prepared to accept it
and do what you have to do, *willingly*. Every nervously
ill person, instead of having "Calais" engraved on their
heart should have that one word, "willingly", there.

Before I answer questions there are still a few
experiences that I want to talk to you about. I've talked
about various symptoms and thoughts, et cetera, but now
I want to speak in more detail about actual experiences
that come with nervous illness. It's not just the symptoms,
it's the indecision, the lack of confidence, the feeling
of disintegration, the feeling of having nothing, nothing
in here [*Dr Weekes points to her heart*], feeling a vacuum,
nothing to get hold of, and when you have had all these
experiences you're very often left with a feeling of being
so bound within yourself, that you cannot get away from
yourself. Whatever you do, your thoughts come back
to yourself, back, back. I have known patients trying
to get out of that trap, to start counting madly: one,
two, three, four, five, et cetera—to try to think of
something else that's not themselves. Oh, the little tricks
they play to try and get themselves out of themselves.

You'd be surprised, the middle-aged people who've come to me complaining of that: famous people, you'd know some of them if I told you their names. While this is an exhausting, bewildering experience, it, perhaps more than any other experience, convinces the sufferer that he or she must surely be going crazy. The key to recovery is—DON'T TRY TO COME OUT OF YOURSELF. DON'T TRY TO STOP THINKING THAT WAY. Let your mind do what it wants to do. Go with it. Think inwardly, but do it so willingly that you relieve some of the strain and a lot of the tension. Without tension your mind will regain its "flexibility". You see, a tired mind seems to lose flexibility, and thoughts stick like glue. Surely, when you're tired you will experience how a tune will get on your mind? I can remember, that after my final exams . . . [*A member of the audience interrupts*]

QUESTIONER: Dr Weekes, how much do you attribute to chemical imbalance as opposed to psychological cause?

DOCTOR: I'll answer it simply by saying that in my opinion nervous illness comes first and chemical imbalance follows. Fix the nervous illness and the chemical imbalance will right itself.

I'm talking about the anxiety state, with or without phobias, obsessions, and do not include illnesses that have a known chemical imbalance, such as manic depression and post-natal depression. Some people in the United States of America write to me for help and tell me they have been put on tranquillisers or antidepressants to right a chemical imbalance, and that they have been told that they will have to stay on their tablets "for life". Almost immediately these people have been helped and finally cured of their nervous illness by adequate explanation and a program for recovery, and have had no medication. I stress once more, that in my opinion, nervous illness comes first and chemical imbalance follows: cure the nervous illness and the chemical imbalance will adjust itself.

QUESTIONER: Would you explain a little more about depletion? You said that Jess, the invisible patient, was depleted or had just had a baby, or whatever. So many people in our groups are depleted. Could you just quickly tell what you would say to a person like this, exercise or diet, or good thinking, or just talking to them. What would you say when they say "I'm so depleted, I can't function." How would you get them going?

DOCTOR: First I'd find out *why*, that's essential. There are so many causes of depletion—anaemia, hyperthyroidism, hypothyroidism, diabetes, TB, et cetera, et cetera; they'd have to be very thoroughly examined. If no organic cause was found, I'd try to find out what stress they're under; for example, constant stress at home? They can be living with someone that's always worrying them, and so depleting them. They can have other home worries, and that's the biggest kind of depleter of all: worry. It's very difficult for a person who's happy to become depleted; so your first investigation is to put right what is depleting. And then once you've done that, the rest Nature will do for you. It's just enough food and enough vitamins, and here again, not too many, just a reasonable amount of vitamins. And to help them to get back to do things *while they are depleted*—not to lie on a couch waiting to feel better, because you can get them to walk, perhaps if helped by somebody, and as they walk into the street they gain a lot of confidence doing that, and you'll find they may walk back unaided. And the next day they can begin to . . . Confidence is a funny thing: it builds on effort; it grows only on effort. We're never handed confidence, it has to be gained always. Even people who feel so depleted can still do amazing things once they're interested in what they're doing. I had an operation once, and it was quite a serious one, and I had to go back to work too soon. I had to go back to work as soon as I came out of hospital. [*Dr Weekes looks at her watch*] (It's ten past nine and we've nearly finished!) and I would stand at the bottom of the hill— my rooms were at the top of the hill—and I'd think "I'll never make it, I'll never get to the top of the hill, I'll just never make it!" I was so exhausted; I knew I was, because the operation had been severe, as I said, and I had nearly died. They had me on intravenous fluids for a fortnight and that's a long time to be on intravenous fluids, and I'd lost a stone and a half in weight. Anyhow, I'd get to the top of the hill all right; I'd climb up to my room and my Scottish secretary would have a cup of coffee for me and what we call a "scone". Do you know, that by the end of the day, when I'd seen many patients, I felt so much better than at the beginning of the day when I'd felt so depleted. And by the end of the week, I was better; by the end of a fortnight, I was all right. But if I'd stayed at home and all the time watched myself, thinking "How much can I do? Do I think I ought to do that? Do you think I ought to do this?" I'd probably still be thinking! Does that answer your question?

QUESTIONER: Yes, thank you. I think many people would like to hear that.

ANOTHER QUESTIONER: Can you offer any general advice as to how to deal with a young person who is unwilling to face things that he fears most? You suggest that the way to recover is to become involved with the things that you fear. When he becomes panicky, he will not deal with the panic.

DOCTOR: How old is he?

QUESTIONER: Nineteen.

DOCTOR: Was he ever a normal person?

QUESTIONER: Yes

DOCTOR: How long ago?

QUESTIONER: Oh, about eight years.

DOCTOR: He hasn't been normal for eight years? I think he's a problem for one particular doctor who will be very interested in helping him: he needs a dedicated doctor who will be prepared to take that boy and try and find out what is holding him back, what is actually in his mind, what he is thinking about his illness, and try to get him motivated again. I had a girl like that and they'd sent her home from a psychiatric hospital and said she'd never ever be recovered. For a year I'd pick her up every morning and take her on my rounds (that's when I was a GP). I took her on my rounds every day of the week practically and sometimes even at weekends. I gradually had her back in a job as a typist—she had rheumatism but she could use an electric typewriter. Now, when I first saw her she'd only lie on the bed and wouldn't look even at me; she'd eat food, but she wouldn't do a thing; but I was able, with the attention, to get her finally into my car. Now that boy, if one person could get enough interest in him to get him doing something, he could get better. But here is a big problem. The only advice I can give you here is to advise you to find some doctor who can give him specialised attention. I'm sorry that I can't give you more advice than that now.

QUESTIONER: Do we interfere with recovery if we take

a tranquilliser when we have very, very severe flashes of panic?

DOCTOR: It depends . . . tranquillisation needs individual tailoring; I always say that. If you've been really trying; if you've been exposing yourself to situations that can bring panic—I call this "putting your head on the block"—and if you feel worn out with it all, then it's sometimes a good idea to take a tranquilliser and have a rest from trying. Sometimes tranquillisation for a short while, and I mean perhaps for only one day, with one night's good sleep, can fire you with new determination. This is why I say tranquillisation needs individual tailoring. Now, sometimes it's necessary to let panic have its head and really flash, even if it seems to you that it's burning the very roots of your hair, let it burn. It's necessary to know that you can see a panic flash right through, that you are the master and need no longer fear it. This means that you know how to take the panic flash: let your body loosen, let it flop, and take the flash with utter, utter acceptance. I've always said that true peace lies on the other side of panic, never on this side. This is why I always say "use tranquillisers with discretion, never as a continuing prop."

QUESTIONER: Dr Weekes, my mother has had phobias for 50 years; is it possible to cure a woman of that age when she's been ill for so long?

DOCTOR: Yes, if you can get the right person to save her. What does she do with her time? Is she alone in the house all day?

QUESTIONER: She works in the house.

DOCTOR: That's a very heavy problem. You'll need a very dedicated doctor to help you there. If you could get your mother involved in outside groups; it's absolutely necessary for her to gradually mix with people. Every day she should be with people, for a start. With groups of people—she should not be left alone in the house all day.

QUESTIONER: She's on the telephone a lot.

DOCTOR: But the people with whom she talks on the telephone—are they cheerful people? Do they do something to help her? Do you think they'd help you find groups that she could work with for a while? Could they do something to help her?

QUESTIONER: She prefers the company of family and doesn't want to meet strangers.

DOCTOR: She's rooted in it, isn't she? Does she live with you and your wife?

QUESTIONER: No, my father died and now we have to make that decision.

DOCTOR: But she might be better living in a home with a lot of other people, old people. I had one patient who fought against going into this kind of home, but I finally got her there, and when I went to see her, the first thing she said to me was "Why didn't you send me in sooner? I can get four for bridge every day." So I would be inclined to seriously think about putting her— I don't mean an old home where they're all lying about doing nothing—I mean where they're alive and up and doing things. She'll never get better living on her own, never.

QUESTIONER: Can you tell me the difference between free-floating anxiety and a phobia?

DOCTOR: Free-floating anxiety means that you are so anxious that wherever you look you see something extra to be anxious about. You can get rid of one source of fear, only to find it almost immediately somewhere else.

It's the state you are in, actually, that is the trouble. Sensitisation will put you into that state. A phobia is a recurring fear, out of all proportion. It's usually a fear of some particular thing, for example, a fear of spiders, a fear of cats; that's a phobia. That's the difference.

QUESTIONER: Do you think there's a link between hormones and nervous illness, which includes phobias?

DOCTOR: Well, there certainly is at the change of life, when the glands get a bit unbalanced. And again, after the birth of a child. I think then, yes, there is.

QUESTIONER: I was affected by the birth of my baby. What do you think we should do? Take vitamins and things?

DOCTOR: I think: eat good food, and know what's happening to you and remember that it will pass, it will pass. Understanding is a great help, and so is some help from friends. If you are depressed after the birth of a baby, you should see your doctor and have a talk to him about it, because post-natal depression is an entity on its own, and it may need special treatment.

[Dr Zane questions Dr Weekes; Dr Weekes nods her head in assent]

DR ZANE: But I think that what you're hearing here from Dr Weekes is that understanding what's happening to you is very important. We talk about "hormones" or "psychology"—that makes no sense. Because if I'm thinking something that has a deleterious effect coming down at me, and if I believe that, will I not have some hormonal changes? Will I not be affected? Of course I would. And then, who knows what the effect of that hormone is on how I'm going to perceive things? How will I react to things? And will not that effect some more hormonal changes? I don't think you can look for a single cause—you've got to look for a system, and the way a human being reacts, and I think that Dr Weekes's efforts would indicate that, right through it, try to accept it, try to recognise that in the end it doesn't matter. She's trying to give you a point of view that will allow you to reorganise hormonally, because if you continue to see dangers ahead you're going to continue to be activated hormonally in ways that will distort the world. Her statement that the person will even begin to see things differently—might see a nun as a man—because of a little change, or something like that; these distortions in perception are definitely related to hormonal changes. But they can come about by the way a person is regarding things and the way that they are reacting to things. So it's very complicated, and I feel that in the end when a person understands the system that's going on, and can accept the fact that there are these changes that go with ideas, they can ride through it better and then come into a different balance. But they'll get frightened, as Dr Weekes is suggesting, based on memory, but then I say the context is restored. The person says, "Oh, I've had it before. Dr Weekes says this about it, so it's something that's really not as dangerous as I feel. I'm going to try to deal with it." It's restoring the perspective that changes our hormones, so I don't want you to think that it's that simple. I think that today's psychiatry [is] almost giving across the idea that people will be comprehended through a hormone. It will never be comprehended through any hormone. But a hormone will have an effect on a person, and it's not just a person, it's a person that Dr Weekes is suggesting too, in a social context. If you have certain kinds of people, if you have a doctor who might go visit a person and devote himself, as Dr Weekes did to this young lady, then you might find the whole system being restored. It's a systemic problem, and the system is not just in the person, it's also in the society that we live in, and I feel that's something that we have to deal with. [*Dr Zane turns to Dr Weekes*] I hope you don't mind my chipping in here, Dr Weekes?

DOCTOR: I enjoy it. [*Much applause from audience*]

QUESTIONER: I have had periods of blackouts, Dr Weekes. Things become very black and ugly and dirty. I feel very, very uncomfortable. What do you think of the tranquilliser Meloril?

DOCTOR: Well, what am I supposed to say about the blackouts first? When do you get them?

QUESTIONER: About every two or three months, and they last a day or two.

DOCTOR: Do you mean you're completely blacked out for a whole day?

QUESTIONER: Not blacked out, but looking at things . . . they look very dirty and ugly.

DOCTOR: Well, that's not a blackout, is it? You see, it's just a change of reality, that's all. That would be a symptom of fatigue, a part of your tension. That's all that is, just a fatigue symptom. You see, we doctors stick to the tranquillisers we know. Meloril I have used back when I was a GP, but I didn't use it very much. I find one has to be so careful of it lowering blood pressure—if a person takes it and stands a good deal, their blood pressure may fall; then again I haven't had enough experience of Meloril to really talk about it. You know, as a doctor, my aim is also to cure my patients using as few tranquillisers as is possible. I had a few that I used, and these I stuck to, because I knew their effects so well. I was never an adventurous doctor when it came to trying different tranquillisers.

QUESTIONER: Are there any recommendations you would make for a person who is afraid of anaesthesia?

DOCTOR: I wonder how many of us are not afraid of anaesthesia. Is anybody here not afraid of going through operations? [*Very few hands go up*] I think the majority dislike anaesthesia, and undergoing an operation, don't you. But you want me to do something for you?

Well, I'll tell you something, There were two patients: one was the patient of another doctor, and he was having part of his tummy removed. When he came out of the anaesthetic, he made such a terrible hullabaloo, he had all the nurses around him; and there was another old man in the bed next to him, and he said to me (he was my patient), "When I have my operation, I'm not going to go on like that!" and I said "No, Bill, because you didn't go on like that—your operation was this morning!" And another patient—my own cousin—had gall stones out, and when I went to see her in the afternoon, she said "Claire, when are they going to take them out?" "They're out, Eva, you had three beauties!" [*Dr Weekes turns to the questioner*] So why are you frightened of anaesthetics? You see, no sooner is the anaesthetic injected—I mean the pentothal—than you've got your eyes wide open again. What are you so frightened of? You have the equivalent of an anaesthetic every night when you go to sleep. What's the difference?

QUESTIONER: How do you deal with feelings of guilt, Doctor?

DOCTOR: How do I deal with feelings of guilt? Oh, boy! [*Laughter*] Well, sometimes you don't, and I tell you, when you're 80 you look back [*Laughter*], and I said to myself to cheer myself up one day, "Now, I'm going to try to think of some of the good things I've done," and you know, I couldn't, I just couldn't! I tried to write them down and look at them. But you know, you think of all the things you should not have done! When I was about eight, I remember meeting my father coming off the boat at the wharf with three or four other men. And I walked up to my father and asked him for some pocket money, and he gave it to me. When he came home he gave me such a lecture for asking him for money in front of other people, when he couldn't very well refuse. I felt so guilty. Now, at 80, I still feel guilty over that! But, joking aside, if it's a big guilt—what you have to remember is that you did it at a time when you were a different person. Everyone of us, I think, has done something that has left us feeling guilty. But given the time all over again, if we could begin as we are now, we would not do it. However, if we remained as we were then, the chances are that we'd still do it. I think maturing means growing up accepting yourself as you were, trying to be a little bit kind to yourself. I think that if it's something that can be told and confessed—good! Then get it off your chest, as long as it doesn't hurt the person to whom you're confessing! You've got to be so careful that you're not just getting it off your chest and on to someone else's! Forgiveness, you ask me—I could write a book about it. But you don't want a book tonight, do you? [*Laughter*]

[*Doctor turns to questioner*]

You know what to do about your guilt?

QUESTIONER: Sometimes I feel I can handle it, and sometimes I can't.

DOCTOR: If it involves other people it's difficult, isn't it?

But then, you can be a nicer person to them; you can make it up in many ways; but, boy, you can get tired of making up and making up; but there it is. And I'll tell you one thing: if you have an old mother or an old father, or a relative who's sick, be as kind and nice to them as you can, because when they're dead you can't bring them back to tell them how much you loved them, or how you wish you'd been kinder to them. It's terribly important to show old people that you love them now. So many of my friends are 80 and over now, and in our letters and cards we are especially nice to one another. We don't want to wait for them to die and say "Oh, I did love Bill," you know? I just put something nice at the end, and they've all caught the habit; they're all doing it. We all have things on our conscience. You know, the old idea of having a priest to tell it to—if you can get a wise priest—is a very good idea.

QUESTIONER: How do you define "a full recovery"?

DOCTOR: Well, to me a full recovery is a person who's able to feel the symptoms, the fears, the experiences that they had when ill, but have them no longer matter. You see, any stress that you go through will bring back symptoms, because they are the symptoms of stress. But when you get them and you can say to yourself "Ha ha! I know you, I've had you before, and you no longer throw me into a tizz!" then you're recovered. "Recovered" does not mean perfect peace *all the time*, because none of us has it; but recovery is coping with yourself as you are, and being able to. Does that satisfy you?

QUESTIONER: Dr Weekes, is it easier to handle a phobia, a new phobia that's been diagnosed, versus an old one that you've learned to live with and have had for a long time?

DOCTOR: Yes, it is easier, but only because the old one has made an engraved pattern which will keep recurring, and when it recurs you will have to keep repeating how you have learnt to cope with it. There's much more repetition and time needed to cope with an old, well-established phobia. You can forget a new one so much more easily. However, when you lose your fear of the repetition, even though momentarily it may strike fear, don't immediately think "It's back!" Think that it's only repeating itself, like onions. Repeat if necessary, but don't be afraid of repeating. It's usually the fear of the repetition that causes the tension. It's by no means always the actual nature of the phobia that causes the tension. It's so often the fact that it seems to be always there. Always ready to claim. Once again, it's the fear of the state you're in. But of course there are certain phobias that do hold an element of fear of the actual thing that's feared; for example, good old spiders, other animals, being on heights. There are many phobias that do definitely hold fear of the phobia itself, and this is where Dr Zane's contextual therapy is very good. You can dissect the fear, find out what it is composed of, and face each element individually. Behaviourism also can cure some phobias; for instance, a dread of cats can be conquered by gradually teaching the sufferer to become used to the sight of a kitten, a lovely little kitten, then to gently perhaps touch it, very carefully, just a little touch; and by these means one can accustom the sufferer even to the sight of a full-grown cat without fearing it. But even here a new phobia will yield quicker to treatment than an old-established phobia. Memory is one of the old bogeys in the woodpile, isn't it?

QUESTIONER: Phobias tend to make you lose self-confidence. How do you start to rebuild that self-confidence?

DOCTOR: It rebuilds itself when you treat the phobia the right way. Confidence automatically comes back when you, yourself, treat yourself, and know what you're doing. It's no good if you depend on outside help, and keep clinging to that as a crutch.

DR ZANE: Now, my own view is Dr Weekes's, that when we talk about phobias we're really talking about something fundamental in human beings, which is the ability to imagine things—imagined dangers—and there is really nothing wrong with imagining the worst kind of dangers. But—if you're alone with it and you start getting those feelings and you don't understand where those feelings are coming from, and what they're about, you can get panicked over that sort of thing, and I think the beginning is to learn that there are other people, and that there are ways of coping, and Dr Weekes has laid them down a long time ago, and others are building on top now, or adding a new concept to hers. Knowing that this is a human thing and does have a structure that can be dealt with, I think we will begin to have a much better effect in the next decade than we've had in the past.

DOCTOR: Thank you, Dr Zane. Now I think it's time for us to close, it's a quarter to ten. Thank you once more, Dr Zane.

DR ZANE: [*After much applause*] We want to thank you all for coming, and Dr Weekes, of course, has laid before us the work of a magnificent woman, who has brought together from her experience, knowledge that will direct us and will help us live in a different world, better than we have lived before. Thank you, Dr Weekes.

6

Talk Given at White Plains Hospital, New York, 1986

On my way home to Australia from London, England, I was asked to speak once more at the White Plains Hospital, Bronxville, New York. I had the manuscript of a new book with me, *More Help for Your Nerves*, which was to be published in a few months in the United States, so I thought I would read a selection from the new book and then answer questions that the audience might ask. However, the audience was obviously anxious for me to finish with the reading (they became restless) and get on with the questions. I asked them if this was what they wanted and they unanimously cried "Yes, please!"

DOCTOR: You want me to talk, not read?

AUDIENCE: Yes, please!

DOCTOR: Well, who's going to ask the first question? Come on . . . [*Silence*] . . . come on now, it's your turn!

QUESTIONER: I was interested in the patient with the trembling hands, and I understood what you said about allowing the fear to be with you, and that it's more important to act normally and not to try hiding the trembling. What I didn't understand from your talk was:

in time, will the trembling go away once you accept the fear of the trembling?

DOCTOR: Oh, yes—if the cause of the trembling is nervous tension. I'll explain what trembling is: it's a nervous reflex. If I tap my leg at the knee, my leg will extend, that jerk is a reflex. Nerve endings in the tendons, and muscles concerned, react and send a message back to my spinal cord, which then sends a message to my legs and says "Jerk", and my leg jerks. Now, in the muscles of the finger there are also nerve endings which react— they react to the stress hormone that your glands secrete when you are upset, frightened, especially, frightened of the trembling. So you're setting up reflex arcs that go back to your spine, then back to your fingers. And that's all trembling is, when it's nervous in origin. Little reflex arcs. Right! How are you going to cure that? Well, the first thing is: reduce the stress. How are you going to reduce the stress? By not worrying about whether your fingers tremble or not. By worrying, you only liberate more stress hormones; so by not worrying, further stress hormones are not liberated, so the nerve endings are not activated, so the arc doesn't take place, so: no trembling.

QUESTIONER: So there is a physiological tie-in which I haven't understood?

DOCTOR: Yes, you didn't understand the way the trembling worked. Well, now I hope you do understand—now we're getting somewhere.

QUESTIONER: You make "accepting" a big part in everything, but how about horror thoughts? How do you learn to accept bad thoughts?

DOCTOR: Try to make them worse—see how bad they can be. I'm not joking. You see, you're afraid of having them, and when you have a specially bad one you think "Oh my God, is that really me thinking that?", and you shake inwardly and a sudden flash of fear seems to destroy you, and you think "I must be really going mad!" All right, try to make yourself go mad! Make the thoughts as horrible as you can. But remember they are only thoughts, only thoughts. Don't let a bad thought frighten you. Don't be afraid to think it! Let it come, don't shrink from it, don't think "I mustn't think those thoughts." THINK THEM. Now, I've had nervously ill nuns who've come to me with that kind of fear: if they get a bad thought they think it is a sin, and they really suffer. One nun said that it was the Devil tempting her, so I answered "Don't try to stop the bad thoughts coming. Don't recoil from them. Let them come! Relax towards them—they are only thoughts, even if you feel propelled. Make them as bad as you can. And accept your reaction to them as part of your illness, your sensitisation. You are still sensitised, and your reactions to the mildest fear are consequently intense, so the thoughts seem shocking." You see, when people have been nervously ill, sometimes the hardest thing to recover from is the habit they've been left with, of thoughts constantly reverting to themselves and their constantly being tortured by outlandish thoughts.

Does that ring a bell for some of you?

THE AUDIENCE MURMURS: Yes.

DOCTOR: Good. Now, everybody makes the mistake of thinking "I mustn't think that, I must try and forget that by doing something else." It's difficult to lose the habit that way. Of course it often gets worse under such tension. You must relax and accept the awareness of self as part of your ordinary thinking. We are all aware of ourselves when we're doing something. But normally, about 10 per cent of our attention is on ourselves and 90 per cent on what we're doing. The nervously ill person, who becomes mentally tired, and has thought inwardly of himself for so many months, thinks of himself 90 per cent and only 10 per cent of what he's doing. All right! Go on doing it this way. It's like a runner who runs a race and touches the finish line—he can't stop then, he has to run on until the momentum dies down. So if you've got that habit, take it with you willingly. Regard what you think, *whatever you think*, as part of your ordinary thinking; accept it as part of your ordinary thinking, not something that you dare not think. When you do this you'll find that gradually you won't even be interested in it. I'll tell you about the man with the lantern, even though I have written about it before. A nervously ill student was staying on a farm, and a neighbour came to visit him. It was night time and he was swinging a lantern in the doorway while he talked to the student. The swinging lantern took the student's attention from himself and he suddenly felt as if a cloud had lifted from his mind. And he thought "Oh, it doesn't really matter what I think, it's the habit that's so upsetting! It's the habit of my thoughts just flying back to me! I could just as well think 'tick', it's the same thing!" And he saw quite clearly that any interest would soon take his mind off that habit, and that finally the habit wouldn't mean a thing—it wouldn't matter! However, when the neighbour left, the curtain that seemed to envelop his mind descended again. Nervous fatigue can seem like a grey curtain between the sufferer and reality. It was as if the student's mind suddenly became thick, muzzy, he couldn't think clearly, he couldn't get his mind off himself. But he had had a moment's insight, so he accepted the muzziness and waited. Even the next day the muzziness was still there; however, during the day the curtain lifted again. For a few days it would descend and lift and descend and lift, but by now the student was relaxed, because he knew that it was going to finally lift because he was no longer tense about its descent. The habit no longer mattered any more. He had hit on the key to kick the habit. Not mattering is the key. And losing tension about the habit is the first step towards finding that key. Now, are there any more questions?

QUESTIONER: Doctor, I get a feeling that somebody is opening my eyes really wide and stretching them until they couldn't stretch any further, and that brings the symptoms of stress. Doctor, am I better trying to find something else to do and not think about this?

DOCTOR: No, you're not, you're not: if you try not to think about it you're just running away. You're magnifying the importance of the feeling while you're running away from it and trying to forget it; the fear of it is hovering in the background most of the time. I know, it's the *consciousness* of the feeling that you're as much afraid of as the actual feeling itself. If you were to stretch your eyes as wide as you could with your hand you wouldn't worry about that. In fact if you couldn't, that'd be the trouble, wouldn't it? Because what would you do if you wanted to show surprise? You'd be handicapped, wouldn't you? No, it's not so much the actual stretching, it's the consciousness of it. You want to be unconscious of that particular feeling. To be unconscious of it, be prepared to relax towards it; don't tense yourself against it; let your mind dwell on it if it wants to, make it part of your ordinary living, accept it. Accept the feeling as being as natural as any other feeling that you have. If you do this, you'll be surprised how quickly it will no longer matter—that old familiar key, no longer mattering. No longer mattering. Utter acceptance leads to no longer mattering. You know, your question was a cousin to the last question about bad thoughts. The treatment is the same. Take the feeling with you with utter acceptance and it will gradually no longer matter.

QUESTIONER: When I was dealing with feelings of unreality, my main problem was when I looked out of a window; why is that? When I looked out of a window, everything was very strange, and that's when it really hit me the hardest.

DOCTOR: Can you tell that loudly enough for the people at the back to hear? Please, stand up and tell the people at the back!

QUESTIONER (*Standing up*): When I was having these feelings of unreality, when I looked out the window, that's when it hit me hardest. I stopped looking out the window. But I wrote a note to Dr Zane and he explained that these were just feelings, and that I'd had a panic disorder for so long, that this was just part of it. And this helped me—I said "I'll nail down this, and if I do look out of the window and have feelings of unreality, I'll know where they come from—from the panic disorder," and little by little I did stop looking out of the window and feeling unreal.

DOCTOR: It was the looking out the window that gave it to you because the world is outside that window. Inside you have the protection of your home, you didn't have to face the world, so you didn't feel unreal there. Outside was the world that one day you would have to face, a world where people moved about, who didn't have the strange feelings that you had; no wonder that seemed unreal to you, even a bit frightening. When you saw the children coming home from school, because you hadn't been interested in that world for a long time, no wonder it seemed unreal, no wonder you shied away from looking out the window. I'm pleased Dr Zane was able to cure you of the habit.

QUESTIONER: I'd like to ask: how does what you've just said apply to anticipatory anxiety, particularly when it relates to travel?

DOCTOR: Anticipatory anxiety is really apprehension, isn't it? If you're agoraphobic and you know you've got to travel, of course you won't be able to stop yourself being apprehensive. You're not in the race to try and stop. At four o'clock you're successfully arguing with yourself and your fears will go, but at three minutes past four, you're back in them again. Well, accept that you're going to be apprehensive until you actually start on that trip. It's part of your state of mind, isn't it? But also know that when you start to do it, the chances are that your anxiety is not as great because it gives way to action, you're more concerned with this now. It's contemplation that's the killer! Recognise that. So go ahead with your contemplation if you feel you must think about it, but also accept the fact that at four o'clock it'll be all right, it'll seem all right, and at five past four, it probably won't. And that's where it is better to get on and do something—get a job done: get to those cupboards you've been meaning to clean out for years. That's a help— do you find that helps you?

QUESTIONER: Yes. I just want to take a second here to say that you practically saved my life: in the mid-seventies I came across your books in the bookshop—I never knew what the word "phobia" meant until then. I picked up your book and travelled all over Europe with it; I had pages marked and knew exactly where to look when I felt bad. You helped me enormously. [*Much applause*] You helped me work my way out of the phobia by myself.

DOCTOR: Good girl. I had a patient in England who wrote to me recently and said that now at last she was able to go to the school prizegiving at her son's school (I've told this story before, but I think it's so good I'll tell it again). She said that her son was so proud to have his mum there at last, that he looked up and said "Gee, Mum, you're doing great!" She added that everything she'd been through was worth it just to hear those words, "Gee, Mum, you're doing great".

QUESTIONER: How do you stop people sabotaging your success when they've been so used to you being part of the furniture, and always there to answer the phone?

DOCTOR: You mean the family, don't you? They can't accept that you're no longer there doing all the jobs you should be doing. How many children have you?

QUESTIONER: I have one, six years old, who is my support person. I finally told him that I was phobic and he said "It's OK" and he accepted me as I am. He helps me practise. [*Much laughter*] It's my husband who cannot understand.

DOCTOR: Have you had a tape recording for him to listen to?

QUESTIONER: I don't know if he would accept that.

DOCTOR: What I used to do when I was in practice, would be to say to the wife "Next time I ring you, get your husband to come to the phone, I'll have a talk to him," and sometimes they wouldn't come, but as a rule they would come and I'd say "Now, you're the sensible one in the family, I want you to help me with your wife!"

To say "You're the sensible one in the family" always did the trick. Then I'd say to him "Of course, you understand that this is this, and that is that," and he of course would try to understand. And in the end I would have a very willing helper. I remember one husband catching up to me as I was going out of the house and saying "Doctor, she's not the girl I married. Always the masha-potato! Why not the chippa-potato?", but he helped in the end, in fact he helped a great deal. But that's how I coped with the husbands and the family. I talk to them and try to get them on my side—that's the only way to do it. If you're thinking of getting a doctor to help you, be sure that you know your doctor well. I remember one doctor who told an enquiring husband not to pamper his wife, that she was neurotic, in fact not to take any notice of her complaining. Know your doctor well. Next question?

QUESTIONER: What is the best attitude a spouse or close family member can have to be supportive of the phobic person?

DOCTOR: First, the spouse must have some idea of what the sufferer is going through; we don't want him to know too much, that becomes a worry for the patient herself; she doesn't want to feel that the family is suffering too. Living with a nervously ill patient is difficult, and the spouse can be almost as nervy as the victim—as a sufferer himself or herself. And the sufferer has to remember that and not expect too much. And the spouse who's trying to help must try not to let his hopes go up and down with the patient, not to have their hopes falsely raised when the patient seems a little better, and then hopelessly dashed again when the patient seems to slip back. They must try and understand that this can happen with nervous illness. Unfortunately, very often the only expression of being able to cope with their spouse's illness is for the husband or wife to seem to cut it right off, have nothing to do with it, to run away from it. I knew one husband who said to his wife "Don't have Dr Weekes's book sitting on the kitchen table again, get rid of that darn thing", or "And don't mention Dr Weekes to me again!" As I say, it's very difficult for a husband or a wife to live with a nervously ill person, who takes a long time to get better [*Dr Weekes hesitates and looks expectantly at the audience*] . . . I'm not quite sure what the question was, I'm lost! [*Laughter*]

QUESTIONER (*Laughing*): I wanted to know what type of ideal attitude should the spouse have, what could they do to help?

DOCTOR (*Laughing*): You mean, when they're *willing* to help?

QUESTIONER: Yes.

DOCTOR: Well, first they have to try to understand the situation. They have to know the program that the wife is working to. A husband must try to share hope and have faith in her program. I think that's about all he can do— be understanding and supportive. If he can do that, he's doing an amazing job. So many of my patients had neither understanding nor support. As I've always said, nervous illness is a very lonely business, because most people cannot expect support from their family. If they get it, it's just fantastic. But as a rule, many nervously ill people get no support from their family. If you want a little more detail as to what I do, I explain to the husband (it usually is the husband, you know) how the sufferer's thoughts, however mild, will bring exaggerated bodily responses and that is why they are so easily upset, so changeable, so moody, so despairing, and how the more they despair, the more intense the suffering becomes and this is where

I explain to him that his behaviour is so important, because of its effect on the sick woman. I explain how reverberated circuits bring a heightened response. Some men understand that very well, if you bring in the electrical description. However, often I use simpler words than those. But often I find that that sentence gives them an insight into what her suffering can be; they seem after that to have more respect for it. "After all, those are electrical circuits," he thinks. I also stress how in my opinion she has been so brave, and that her suffering is not neurotic. I explain how living with her nervous system seems like living with live wires. I must say I do lay it on a bit. I paint a rather lurid picture sometimes, because with some husbands I feel desperate to try and shake their air of superior intolerance. And in all fairness I must add that I do meet sometimes some fantastic husbands, who go to great lengths to understand and help their wives, I must stress that. To answer your question briefly: the family must try to understand and be supportive and comfort, and try not to lose their patience.

QUESTIONER: As far as accepting the symptoms goes, I find that with the rapid heartbeats, I don't think I could encourage them to go faster!

DOCTOR: Heavens, I've never said to encourage your heart to go faster!

QUESTIONER: It's the symptom that scares me, I'm trying to escape from that.

DOCTOR: Have you seen your doctor?

QUESTIONER: Oh yes, many times.

DOCTOR: And he's examined you and said that the fast rate is "only nerves", has he?

QUESTIONER: Yes.

DOCTOR: How fast does it go?

QUESTIONER: 160 sometimes, but mostly around 120.

DOCTOR: 120 isn't terribly fast.

QUESTIONER: It is for me! I have trouble ignoring that!

DOCTOR: I've never asked you to ignore it—it's very difficult to ignore a heart as fast as that; you see, ignoring is not the same as accepting. Accepting means don't be upset, know your heart is racing, but understand that a heart can beat very fast without damaging itself. The more frightened you are of it, the quicker it's going to beat. You know that, don't you? Because the adrenalin that's secreted when you're afraid increases the rate of the heart.

You see, your heartbeat is regulated by two special parts of your nervous system—the parasympathetic and the sympathetic. Remember, it's the sympathetic that stimulates the secretion of adrenalin and that's what makes the heart muscle beat fast. The parasympathetic makes the heart calm down and it is the balance between the parasympathetic and the sympathetic that keeps the heart beating at a normal pace. Now, as soon as you let the quick beating exasperate you, up comes more adrenalin and on goes the heart; and so you keep the whole thing going. You really have got to learn to let it beat without being afraid of it, and I promise you that then it will gradually calm down. Today there are tablets called beta-blockers that can calm a fast heart within about 20 minutes, but—have you been taking beta-blockers?

QUESTIONER: No, I've come here because I'm also phobic about taking tablets. [*Laughter*]

DOCTOR: Perhaps it's just as well, because eventually, if you do take beta-blockers, you'll have to come off them. That in itself could be a bit of a problem.

QUESTIONER: And, Doctor, sometimes I get very slow heartbeats, and that can be very frightening.

DOCTOR: Yes, that's right. That's the parasympathetic taking over—overstimulation of the vagus nerve.

QUESTIONER: I find very slow heartbearts just as frightening as the very quick. I expect my heart to stop.

DOCTOR: Your heart has evolved over millions of years— *you*'re not going to stop it. You're not going to harm it with your thoughts or your fear. You're not as important as all that. Nature's not going to let that wonderful, strong young heart suffer damage because of your fear, your thoughts. We're built to take life's moments of physical suffering while we're young. Nature is not going to stop your heart now—not on your life! Look at all the thousands of years that it took to get you here, and the extra nine months' work your mother did. Your heart will still be going when you're 80— look at the heart I've got, at 83. I can assure you, mine's been through all the palpitations, and the rest of it. Palpitations, although attention-demanding, are really unimportant when only caused by nerves. Also remember, when your nervous heart is beating at 120, you could still play tennis; in fact, while you're playing tennis, it could calm down!

QUESTIONER: Yes, Doctor, I've found that.

ANOTHER QUESTIONER: Dr Weekes, can you comment on ritualistic and obsessive behaviour, how a person can deal with that?

DOCTOR: Well, I could write a book about that. There are two ways of dealing with this: you see, tension is the force behind obsessive behaviour, whether it is ritualistic or not, and the tension is usually so strong that the sufferer, he or she, feels it physically. So he can either reduce that tension by obeying the ritual in *a particular way*, or by confronting it full on, and beating it.

The "particular way" is to obey the ritual willingly. "Willingly" is a wonderful word. It means that you do not castigate yourself while you're doing it, you don't think "You're a fool for doing this, this is a crazy, terrible habit. I don't think I'll ever get rid of this!" If you obey it willingly, really willingly, the tension behind it will gradually go. In the talks I gave in London recently on the BBC [Chapter Two], there was a patient, Anne, who had, as she said, almost "every obsession in the book". The doctors at the psychiatric hospital that she attended were finally so desperate they wanted her to let them do a leucotomy. However, she wouldn't agree to this because she'd seen somebody who'd had one and it hadn't been a success. That was when I talked to her on the telephone: I cured Anne by teaching her to "glimpse". For instance, when a mother has the obsession that she's going to hurt her child, which so many tired mothers get, I teach them to see that what they have at that moment is a very exaggerated reaction to an idea that comes, exaggeratedly intense, because they were sensitised at the moment when they first had that thought—so now every anxious thought is bringing an exaggerated reaction, a terrific reaction! As I said, I've explained to them that, at that moment, it is as if they are two different people: one with the thought, the intense reaction, the fear, and the other one who knows she would never do it. But that one who knows she would never do it seems so weak compared with the other. No wonder she gets terrified. So the one who'd never do it, they feel conscious of only vaguely, while the other, the overpowering feeling, threatens to carry them away.

When they come to me they admit that there is this vague feeling behind the obsessive thought, that of course they would never, ever hurt their child. I teach them that this feeling, the vague feeling, is the one that they must glimpse every day, if only for a second. If they can hold the *feeling* within themselves, if only for a second, that they would never do it, this is what they must practise. It's no good just saying it with their lips to themselves. They have to dig deep within themselves to *feel* the feeling, until they admit to themselves that deep down they know they would never do it.

That is what I call the glimpsing; and they must practise this during the day, giving time to it as one would give time to practising playing the piano, until in the end the glimpse becomes established as reality. And they will find that then, of course, the compulsive thought of doing it grows less and less intense, until it is finally only a thought, without any truth, without any substance or meaning.

Understanding the second way to confront the obsession directly is helped by my taking, as an example, a chocoholic: "glimpsing" seems to make her worse! Especially if the particular chocolates glimpsed are especially tempting! After allowing herself two pieces—conscience and her weight dictate—the thrust towards the rest of the chocolates soon starts. It is a boring urge in her middle (the throne of tension). The more she thinks of the chocolates, the more the thrust gathers force, until it is strong enough to almost lift her from her seat. This is where she must understand that the thrust *is only tension*, and that if she calls its bluff and sees it through (once more, the old acceptance), the force of the tension gradually melts away; oh, it whimpers a bit, but if she is prepared to watch the mounting and wait, it finally dies down and she can even bear to look at the chocolates as she puts them away. She calls tension's bluff; although it appears to be able to mount and mount, *there is a limit* to the mounting, and if she's prepared to wait long enough, the mounting will finally abate. Then the mounting no longer threatens because she knows that she's been there, she's taken it, it goes! And that is the second way to overcome an obsession. You would have those two choices: glimpsing or seeing tension's bluff right through.

An obsession is one of the hardest experiences for a doctor to cope with, there's no question about that. At least, that's been my experience. And these people do need a lot of help from their doctor. At the moment I have a girl ringing me from London. She rings me every day—she has, for three months—and I can talk to her only for a few minutes, because telephone calls are expensive in England and especially expensive from England to America. I gave her my American number before I left England. You see, obsessional people gradually lose trust in themselves; they feel there's an "it" outside themselves that takes command of them. But that old "it" is only tension, and the brain's almost automatic repetitive response to suggestion at a time when the sufferer is vulnerable. As I said in the beginning, I could almost write a book about that, but that's as much as I can tell you tonight.

QUESTIONER: Are repetitive thoughts the same as obsessive thoughts, where you have continuous thoughts that you find difficult to get out of your mind?

DOCTOR: Yes, that's definitely a form of obsession. I have already discussed that this evening. But I will talk about it briefly again. After all, it does seem to be so important to so many of you.

Try not to be afraid of the thoughts coming back;

don't withdraw from them: you do tend to withdraw, you think "Oh my God, here they come again!" Don't do this, go into them and repeat them, *but willingly*. Try not to be afraid of repeating them. You'll find then that if you're doing it willingly you'll finally become interested in other things. When you withdraw from the thoughts, you do this in fear, when you relax towards them, and accept them willingly, the fear gradually goes. The little voice inside you will say "You don't have to be afraid of this. What the heck, it's only a repetitive thing that will be dropped when you don't tense yourself about it." With no tension, there is no encouragement. Very quickly your mind hitches on to other things.

QUESTIONER: How long does it take to cure something like this? Does it come back again and again?

DOCTOR: It depends entirely on your attitude. If you are talking about yourself, then it depends on how you remember what you've been through, and how you react to that memory. It's possible to go for years without even thinking about what you've suffered, and then suddenly something, some happening, may make you remember, and if the memory comes charged with the old suffering, the chances are the shock could make you recoil with fear again. If you relax and remember how you got rid of all these fears before and think "OK, I'll take these memories and the feelings they bring and even the apprehension they bring, I'll take it all willingly." If you relax towards it, go into it, really relax towards it, don't become apprehensive of it—well, not too apprehensive—you'll find that your attention will wander, wander. The recurrence of memory will no longer be a shock and will no longer upset you.

QUESTIONER: How about getting rid of it completely so that the memory never comes back?

DOCTOR: Nobody could promise that, because nobody can anaesthetise memory, can they?

QUESTIONER: No.

DOCTOR: You will probably remember what you suffered; it would be unusual if you didn't, and the suffering can bring back feelings. You see, memory doesn't only bring back thoughts. Severe suffering in the past can bring back the old feelings, or at least ghosts of the old feelings. But don't be bluffed by this. Recognise it as memory, and go towards it. Never withdraw in fear, just remember that. Also go forward willingly, with relaxation towards it, even if it gives you a bit of a shock, even if your automatic response is to be afraid—go through that, that's natural. How could you expect to go through again what you've been through before and be as cool as an iceberg whenever you thought of it again in the future? Don't demand too much of yourself, just understand; that is the big thing, understand it. In doing that, you understand yourself, and you just won't be carried away by the shock.

QUESTIONER: Would you use the same basic technique when treating a young child?

DOCTOR: I would treat a young child a little bit differently. For instance, one young child had a phobia about going up the stairs. She sat at the bottom stair and wouldn't budge. Instead of discussing it with her as I would with an adult, I said "You don't have to climb the stairs if you don't want to. Just sit on the bottom stair. You'll grow out of this fear as you get older. Now, you've never seen a grown-up who can't climb stairs, have you, unless she's had rheumatism or something? As you grow older, even in the next few months, you won't be so afraid of climbing the stairs at all. You never see a grown-up stuck with fear of climbing the stairs!" That little girl lost her fear that very day! I treat children on a sort of tangent, if you know what I mean. I get them to get rid of their fear by debunking the fear for them. Take the bogeyman away that's frightening them and then they'll get over that fear. Treating children is not easy. I make it sound easy, but it's not easy. Children can be so clever. But I usually find the way, and tailor it to the individual child.

QUESTIONER: Some people that I know have mentioned to me that they've had something of an alcohol and drug problem which they got before they had joined some group or other to cope with these problems, but after joining the group they said they developed a phobia about the alcohol and drugs—after they had joined the group. Can you explain that?

DOCTOR: I'm not clear of your meaning.

QUESTIONER: Well, it's kinda like they had an illness while dependent on drugs and alcohol, but they feel somehow that they've anaesthetised themselves with the alcohol and the drugs instead of dealing with the phobia. Then when they stop drinking or stop drugging they have this accentuated phobic reaction, so that they're suddenly afraid of travelling, like agoraphobics, and things like that, even with the support of other people. For instance, I mean, they don't have the symptoms when they're in AA; they're pretty well adjusted to that, but if they stay away from the meetings, or talk to other people . . .

DOCTOR: Then they have an attack?

QUESTIONER: Yes, if they've gone to the meeting, it takes them outside themselves, that's my point.

DOCTOR: You mean that once they're away from the shelter

of an AA or other group, it's very hard for them to cope with their illness on their own?

QUESTIONER: Yes, that's what I mean.

DOCTOR: But you know, for permanent cure, they will have to cope on their own. To be permanently cured, you have to be able to bear yourself—you have to be able to cope with your symptoms through understanding and accepting. The cure must lie there, not in taking drugs or alcohol or *depending* on the support of others. That's not a cure at all. You've got to get it from within yourself. I'm not talking now about drugs or alcohol, I'm talking now about nervous illness. You've got to earn your little voice that says "You've been here before, old chap, you know the way." That little voice is earned only by your own effort and becomes gradually so strong within you that you can stand anything and will always find the little voice ready to help—that's why I'm glad recovery takes time. That's why I'm glad when people have setbacks, because in each setback that little voice is strengthened, by more and more experience; that's the important thing—to have within yourself the knowledge that you can do it, you can depend on yourself. That's so important.

QUESTIONER: Could you not be phobic and have obsessive thoughts and still not be an obsessive person? Phobic people have scary thoughts, and they dwell on scary thoughts, and yet an obsessive person is also like this— he dwells on scary thoughts, so how is it that a phobic person is not necessarily an obsessive person?

DOCTOR: Phobias and obsessions do overlap. They merge into each other. When you have a distinct phobia you simply have fear of a certain thing, and when you have a distinct obsession you not only have a fear of something but you also have a compelling force within yourself. For instance, a person who has a phobia about a particular window definitely avoids that window, but a person who had a compulsion about that window feels that he has to go past it again and again. That I think is the big difference between the two of them: one is linked with avoidance, and the other is linked with compulsion to confront.

[*Dr Zane speaks to Dr Weekes*]

DOCTOR: Dr Zane asks me to give some of the men a chance to question me.

QUESTIONER: If you're afraid of an animal that you don't see very often, for instance, a snake, is there a way to check yourself before you panic, is there a way to overcome this fear?

DOCTOR: Yes, there is; but snakes at any time are hard to be unafraid of, aren't they?

QUESTIONER: Well, we don't see them every day, do we?

DOCTOR: No, especially in New York. When a therapist tries to help a patient with a fear of animals, he must begin gently. For example, starting with fear of snakes, we could take the skin of a dead snake and help the patient to try to look at it. In time we may get him to touch it, you see?

QUESTIONER: I don't think I could even get to the stage of looking at it. I don't even know why I've had this problem, and I've had it from childhood.

DOCTOR: I understand. But you want very much to get rid of it, don't you? And that's a big incentive, that alone will help you. Dwell on your urge to get better. So think, "Well, I'm a big strong man (and you are a big strong man), so I've got to open my eyes and look at this thing. I've got to do that sooner or later." So you do as Dr Zane says—you do it on the rungs of a ladder, bit by bit. And in the end, I can assure you, you can look at the whole snake. I've never been able to get rid of my fear of a live snake in the bush (has anybody?), especially when it's coming towards me! I think we'd get better results with a cat, when we can go through a period of taking first a kitten, and learning to touch its fur—I have seen this succeed completely.

QUESTIONER: I finished your book this morning—it was a remarkable piece of work. How do you tell someone who's had the panic attacks for five years—I'm sure you've had patients who've panicked for as long as this— how do you tell them to let time pass? I've been given to understand that an anxiety–panic–depression attack is the most difficult thing a person can experience and, not trying to be disrespectful, you've done marvellous work, you've had a great and illustrious career, and I hope you're back with us 10 years from tonight, maybe 20 years from tonight, but how do you tell them to let time pass? And I have one more question—I bought your book, I thought I was buying a mystery. It's OK, but there were portions that were kinda like a mystery. At the very end I still wasn't sure about this "float" process: how do you have the most difficult experience of your lifetime and still "float"? What is the process?

DOCTOR: Well, take one specific example: take a person who is agoraphobic and tries to go into a shop, for instance. They tend to become rooted to the ground, so that they cannot move their muscles. They literally feel they cannot move, and what they do is always the wrong thing, they think "I will go! I will go! I'll b----y well get there!", and you know, when you severely tense a muscle it's hard to move it. And these people find that they've locked themselves into inaction. In fact, they feel they can't budge! Now if they were to think "Float, don't fight, float, think of 'floating' in, let your body go 'loose'; loosen all those tight muscles and float, f-l-o-a-t in," they would find then that they could get into that shop. The very thought of floating relaxes. You'll probably remember the woman I tried to get to buy me some fish: she said "But I haven't been in a shop for years! I can't go in there!" I said "Float in, don't force your way in— don't fight to go in, float!" and she came back with the fish and said "I'm still floating! Do you want me to float for something else?"

As for letting time pass: letting more time pass is usually the last thing these people want to do. Remember that before I have asked them to let time pass, I have made sure that they understand what they're trying to cope with, that they understand that I'm teaching them what sensitisation is, that they must be willing to accept their feelings, to float and not fight. And they've got to become pretty well au fait with those aspects before they can understand and appreciate that time will still have to pass before their new understanding will bear fruit. Once they've attempted to do this thing, they will then understand clearly why time has to pass. It can't be done in a day, it's like climbing a greasy pole: you go up two feet and you fall down one foot, so that's going to take time, isn't it? You see, they've been ill for so long, naturally they want to be well quickly, and the last thing they want to do is to let more time pass. But they've got to do just that. So they may as well understand that from the beginning, and be prepared for it. They should tuck the days behind them, "That's another day gone!", be prepared for more days to have to go, and not be like the man in one of my books who was going for a holiday to Honolulu for two weeks and said "I'm going to give myself those two weeks and I'll be better at the end of it; I'll be so much better by then, I'll be able to go back to work, cured!" But he wasn't and he couldn't. You have to let as much time pass *as is necessary*, as much time pass as recovery takes. There's no alternative, so let it pass willingly. You see, you've got to have enough time to build normality within yourself. Time, time, time, to become used to being normal. You can't suddenly step out of nervous illness as you would a cloak—although I've seen some people do it—however, the majority cannot suddenly step out of their illness. They will feel better one day, perhaps ill the next. They have to be prepared for all this. Only the passage of time will help the program that I have given you to consolidate your recovery. Even if someone you love dies, you know that gradually you will become reconciled to this and adapted to it. Recovery is like that—you have to become adapted to it.

Some people can be magnificently better one day, go into town, ride a bus, do everything. And yet the next day they can start to go out, and feel worse than ever. All right, that's when they must say "Let more time pass." Recovering from nervous illness is letting time consolidate what they have gained, until they are on firm ground, and the ground gets firmer and firmer. Do you remember, in one of my books, the patient who had been two years in her house, whom the husband could not get out, and who finally accompanied him to see me in my rooms in Sydney? I explained panic to her, she went downstairs on her own and bought jelly beans and came back. When she rang me the next day she said "I'll never be cured, because I can't panic." Remember that she said she went to the top of the AMP

Building, up 14 storeys and looked over, and couldn't even panic then! Now, that's years ago and she's still fine. You see, I took all the fear away from her—she was no longer afraid of panicking.

Now I must tell you that you can panic even though you have no fear of it. That's almost like a confession, isn't it. You see, when you're severely sensitised, a cold blast of wind can bring a flash of panic, and that's where it is difficult for a nervously ill person to understand what it's all about. When they're so vulnerable to returns of panic; it's hard for them to understand why, but at least they do understand that they have to let more time pass. And to practise, and to remember that if they fail they can always have another go. Failure is only failure when you accept it as failure! That's one acceptance I don't want you to make. [*Dr Weekes turns to the questioner*] Does that help you with that question?

QUESTIONER: Yes, it does. Thank you, Doctor.

DOCTOR: This old girl's getting tired. Half past seven, half past eight, half past nine, I've been talking for two hours.

DR ZANE Thank you, Doctor Weekes, I'm glad myself that there are those of you who spoke up when they were a little bit disconsolate about Dr Weekes just reading from her book. When Doctor Weekes started answering your questions I could feel you all wake up and Doctor Weekes could address herself to the answers and we could feel again the vibrant, active, alert reponses that are so typical of Dr Weekes. So I want to thank the audience for being here and I want to especially thank Dr Weekes once again.

[*Dr Weekes thanks the audience and also turns and thanks Dr Zane*]

DR CLAIRE WEEKES SPEAKS

Dr Weekes gives further help on audio cassettes and a video for sufferers from "nerves".

The audio cassettes are called:

HOPE AND HELP FOR YOUR NERVES
GOOD NIGHT, GOOD MORNING
NERVOUS FATIGUE – UNDERSTANDING AND COPING WITH IT
MOVING TO FREEDOM, GOING ON HOLIDAY

The video is called:

PEACE FROM NERVOUS SUFFERING

The audio cassettes are available from:

Australia
Claire Weekes Publications Pty Ltd
PO Box 377
Woden ACT 2606

United Kingdom
Relaxation for Living
168–170 Oatlands Drive
Weybridge
Surrey KT13 9ET

USA
Living Growth Foundation
PO Box 48751
St Petersburg
Florida 33743
Tel: 813 345 8831

The video is available from:

United Kingdom and Australia
Pacific Recordings
32 Woodside Drive
Cottingley
Bingley
West Yorkshire BD16 1RF

USA
Living Growth Foundation
PO Box 48751
St Petersburg
Florida 33743
Tel: 813 345 8831

More Help for Your Nerves

Dr Claire Weekes is acclaimed throughout the world for her work on nervous illness. In this book she gives hope and invaluable advice to sufferers.

Dr Weekes believes that stress can produce symptoms and experiences that in time become more important to the nervously ill person than the original cause of the illness. Sufferers can become so concerned with, and afraid of, the state that they are in that they become trapped in a cycle of suffering.

In *More Help for Your Nerves*, Dr Weekes reveals the common, almost inevitable pattern of development of nervous symptoms. In particular, she analyses and explains nervous fatigue and shows that by understanding this fatigue – and following the principles she describes – it is possible to reverse the pattern and so bring recovery.

Peace from Nervous Suffering

The nervously ill person too often finds hope followed so quickly by despair and disappointment that he or she may think, 'Dare I hope again?' In this book Dr Claire Weekes not only sustains hope throughout, but also backs it with a positive programme for recovery.

The book offers help to those suffering from the commonest kind of nervous illness – the anxiety state (often called nervous breakdown). In addition, Dr Claire Weekes offers especial advice to those whose illness is dominated by a particular fear – agoraphobia.

If your suffering seems unique to you, and if you have so far failed to find a satisfactory explanation for it, then this is essential reading for you. By practising Dr Claire Weekes' method, you can learn how to go forward and take your place among people without fear.

Simple Effective Treatment of Agoraphobia

Agoraphobia, in its strictest sense, is a fear of open spaces. But for Dr Claire Weekes – the bestselling author of *Self Help for Your Nerves* – it has wider implications. It is a condition, primarily of women, in which there is an incapacitating fear away from the safety of home. This may occur particularly in crowded or isolated places or anywhere where sufferers cannot make a quick escape or get help promptly should their fears – as they think – grow beyond them. It includes a fear of travelling.

While this book is primarily concerned with the treatment of agoraphobia, the advice given can also be used in treating many people in an anxiety state, uncomplicated by agoraphobia.

SELF HELP FOR YOUR NERVES	0 7225 3155 9	£4.99	☐
MORE HELP FOR YOUR NERVES	0 7225 3202 4	£4.99	☐
PEACE FROM NERVOUS SUFFERING	0 7225 3201 6	£4.99	☐
SIMPLE EFFECTIVE TREATMENT OF AGORAPHOBIA	0 7225 3156 7	£4.99	☐

All these books are available from your local bookseller or can be ordered direct from the publishers.

To order direct just tick the titles you want and fill in the form below:

Name: _____

Address: _____

_____

_____ Postcode: _____

Send to: Thorsons Mail Order, Dept 3, HarperCollins*Publishers*, Westerhill Road, Bishopbriggs, Glasgow G64 2QT.
Please enclose a cheque or postal order or your authority to debit your Visa/Access account —

Credit card no: _____

Expiry date: _____

Signature: _____

— to the value of the cover price plus:
UK & BFPO: Add £1.00 for the first book and 25p for each additional book ordered.
Overseas orders including Eire: Please add £2.95 service charge. Books will be sent by surface mail but quotes for airmail despatches will be given on request.

24 HOUR TELEPHONE ORDERING SERVICE FOR ACCESS/VISA CARDHOLDERS – TEL: 0141 772 2281.